D1631675

Reading R R Room *Companion*

· ·

C O N S I S T I N G *of*

a rare and valuable

COLLECTION *of*

diverse C U R I O S I T I E S

············· *acquired by and for* ·············

Henry Wellcome

with A GREAT VARIETY OF BOOKS

Written & compiled by Anna Faherty

First published in 2014 by Wellcome Collection, part of
The Wellcome Trust, 215 Euston Road, London NW1 2BE.

**wellcome
collection**

www.wellcomecollection.org

The Reading Room combines the strengths of Wellcome Collection's exhibitions
and events and the Wellcome Library in an evolving public space full of
opportunities to look, read, collect and share. It is part of the Wellcome Trust,
a global charitable foundation dedicated to achieving extraordinary improvements
in human and animal health.

Reading Room Companion Copyright © The Wellcome Trust 2014

All images reproduced in this book are reproduced courtesy
of the Wellcome Library, except where stated.

10 9 8 7 6 5 4 3 2 1

The moral right of the authors has been asserted.

Unless otherwise attributed, the text for this book is available for re-use under
a Creative Commons Attribution Only (CC-BY) 4.0 licence. Many of the images
are also available under the same licence. Visit wellcomeimages.org for more
information.

A CIP catalogue record for this book is available from the British Library.

ISBN 978-0-9570285-5-5

Editor: Anna Faherty
Research: Ruth Blue and Julia Nurse
Additional content: Hugh Aldersey-Williams and Ruth Garde
Graphic design: Objectif
Editorial: Sal Davies and John Watson
Photography: Richard Everett, Tom Farnetti, Ben Gilbert and Jon Stokes

Printed and bound in Belgium by Cassochrome

Any omissions and errors of attribution are unintentional and will, if notified in
writing to the editor, care of the Wellcome Trust, be corrected in future printings.

*Read in an attractive room,
and from time to time let
your eyes gaze upon beautiful
objects so that you will come
to love what you read.*

Profiat Duran, writing in
Maaseh Ephod, 1403

Reading Room contents
Introducing the Reading Room *p.VIII*

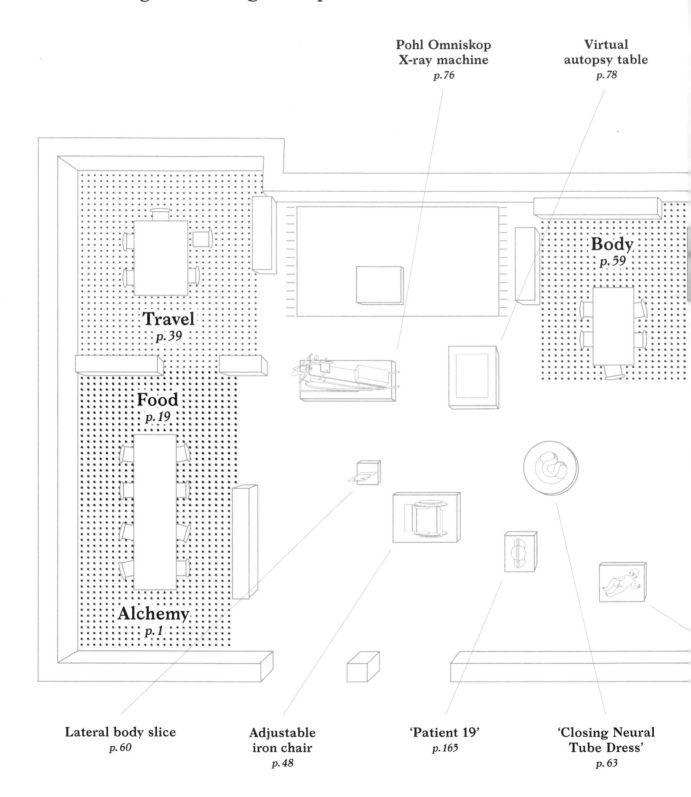

Pohl Omniskop
X-ray machine
p.76

Virtual
autopsy table
p.78

Body
p.59

Travel
p.39

Food
p.19

Alchemy
p.1

Lateral body slice
p.60

Adjustable
iron chair
p.48

'Patient 19'
p.165

'Closing Neural
Tube Dress'
p.63

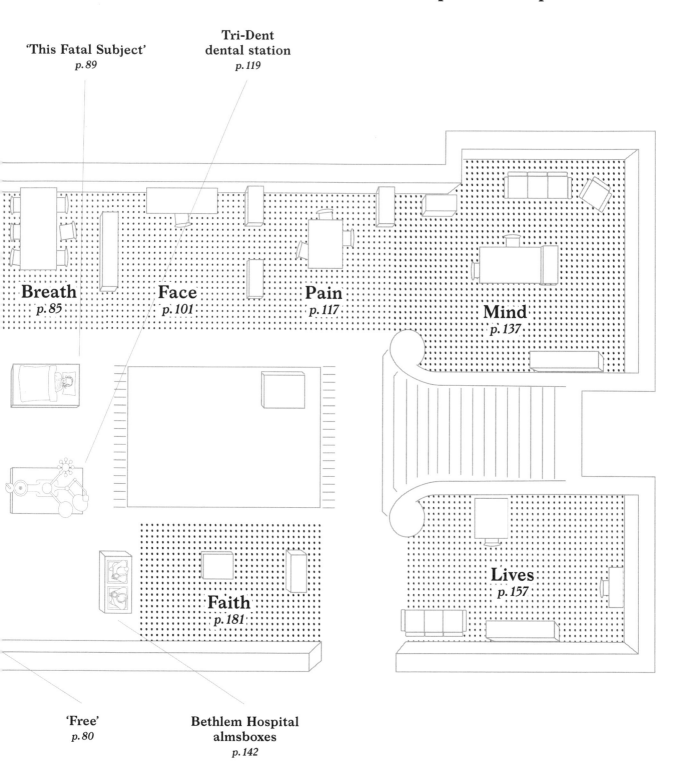

Painting wall contents

'Saint Expeditus'
p.194

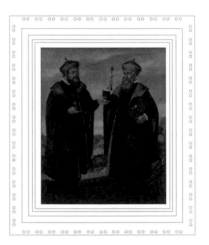

**'Saint Cosmas and Saint
Damian in a Landscape'**
p.196

**'A Woman in Bed
in a Sick Room'**
p.190

**'Apotheosis
of an Ecclesiastic'**
p.206

**'Saint Cosmas
and Saint Damian Dressing
a Chest Wound'**
p.132

'The Sense of Touch'
p.134

'A Blacksmith Extracting
a Tooth'
p. 118

'The First Use of Ether
as an Anaesthetic in
Dental Surgery'
p. 121

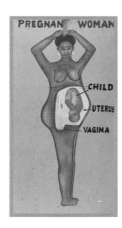

Pregnant woman from
the shack of a voudun
practitioner
p. 70

'A Man Holding
an Écorché Statue'
p. 64

A dissected man with
separate sections of the brain
p. 68

Two dissected men with
a separate section of viscera
p. 69

'An Alchemist
in his Laboratory'
p. 12

'An Alchemist'
p. 14

'An Alchemist
in his Laboratory'
p. 13

Introducing the Reading Room

Welcome to the Reading Room. If Wellcome Collection is home for the incurably curious, this space is designed to nurture those most gravely afflicted by the desire to know just a little bit more.

Like the rest of Wellcome Collection, the Reading Room draws inspiration from our founder, the pharmacist, entrepreneur and avid collector Henry Wellcome. The room was originally designed as a Hall of Statuary and formed part of his sprawling museum, with marble busts rubbing up alongside totem poles and anatomical figurines. But Wellcome was not just obsessed with objects. His initial passion was as a bibliophile, and after his death the Hall of Statuary was reinvented as part of his library, crammed with bookcases and card catalogues. From time to time there were experiments with exhibitions alongside the bookshelves and readers' desks, but the main purpose of the room was solitary, scholarly study – a place for consuming and producing text.

In its latest incarnation, we have tried to knit together this split heritage to create a place that champions both sides of Wellcome's collection. It celebrates both the tradition of exhibition visiting – of looking, talking and sharing – and that of the library, of reading, touching, thinking, writing and creating. We hope that you will find inspiration in the combination of these two very common (but usually separate) cultural spaces and indulge your curiosity in multiple ways. Perusing an exhibit or artwork may lead you to browse bookshelves and drawers, or the books and other resources in the room might prompt you to look anew at the objects on display. The room is full of invitations to leave your own mark so that, like all great libraries, the Reading Room will grow to be as much a product of its user as its designer.

Since opening in 2007, Wellcome Collection has made great efforts to shine an intriguing light on the visual and material culture associated with medicine and health. The Reading Room carries on that habit of experimental exhibition-making. At the same time, we have also been inspired by the rekindled excitement about the value that libraries bring to our lives. Despite (or perhaps because of) economic and political vicissitudes, there seems to be a growing number of people who see the benefit of reinventing and reinvesting in publicly accessible libraries.

By bringing together the gallery and the library, we also hope to encourage other, more social, uses, as the room and its contents suggest points of departure for conversations and other shared activities. We've tried to fashion an environment full of intriguing things that will prompt and provoke you to respond (and to do so in ways that we haven't tried to predict or constrain). We've chosen ten themes, over a hundred objects and over a thousand books to act as eclectic, exotic springboards for an exploration of the human condition, but the success of the Reading Room will rest in what you make of it and from it.

We were torn in our curatorial instincts about how to interpret what can be found in this space. We were eager to keep labelling and instructions to a minimum, but still wanted to provide as much context about the material housed here as we could. We did not want to print a book on the walls, but had a book's worth of ideas to share. This volume – a companion compendium shelved within the Reading Room – has got us out of that fix. We hope it will inspire you to find and experience as much of the room's contents in as rich a way as time and appetites allow. And should you find yourself browsing a copy in some other room or space, we still hope you will find dipping into its varied pages rewarding. In either case, enjoy!

Ken Arnold
Head of Public Programmes

Simon Chaplin
Head of Wellcome Library

'An Explosion in a Laboratory'
Artist and date unknown

Alchemy

The word 'alchemy' commonly conjures up images of misguided loners engaged in industrious folly. Working in crowded cabinets of curiosities, these forerunners of the 'mad scientist' trope communicated in cryptic language and struggled to make ends meet. But alchemy is more than this: at its heart is a holistic way of viewing the world, where matter is in a continuous state of flux.

Originating in ancient Greece and Egypt, and taking its name from the Arabic *al-kīmiyā*, alchemy was a well-established intellectual perspective in Europe between the fifteenth and eighteenth centuries. Its exponents were motivated by diverse aims. Some pursued the elusive philosopher's stone that might turn lead into gold, others developed successful metallurgical and manufacturing processes; some searched for the elixir of life, others produced practical medicines to heal the sick.

While some alchemists toiled solely for the pure purpose of acquiring and reforming knowledge, others might be money-hungry noblemen, labouring practitioners or fraudulent 'puffers'. United by a penchant for reading, writing, making and doing, alchemists of every type sought to transform the world around them and, indeed, themselves.

With the eighteenth-century emergence of the discipline of 'chemistry', activities probing the nature and structure of matter, or processes harnessing its transformations, were recategorised as 'science'. 'Alchemy' became more of a pejorative label, associated with smelly and dirty fraudsters and linked with magic, witchcraft and the occult. At any time, unravelling the truth behind alchemy is a challenging task, thanks to its multiple meanings and the deception and secrecy employed by many practitioners and writers.

> *Look, and you will find [the alchemist's] primary transmutation to be of himself: a goldsmith becomes a goldmaker, an apothecary a chemical physician, a barber a Paracelsian, one who wastes his own patrimony turns into one who spends the gold and goods of others.*
>
> Michael Maier in *Examen Fucorum Pseudo-Chymicorum*, 1617

'An Explosion in a Laboratory'

'An Explosion in a Laboratory'
Oil on canvas
Artist and date unknown
RRa0089 / 45090i Wellcome Library

This scene is unlikely to be a representative view of the everyday reality of alchemy. Contrary to the spectacular image of wizards and magicians, alchemists actually worked slowly and patiently. They repeated the same processes over and over again, waiting and watching for changes.

However, alchemical equipment could be costly, and potential wealthy patrons might be wooed by the theatre of an impressive result like that shown here. Alchemists also employed elaborate tactics to disguise what they were doing; smoke and mirrors like this might be just the trick to confuse or distract those who wanted to steal their secrets.

🔍 The dark arts

This painting is part of a contrasting pair. One work shows beneficial activities, such as the production of medicines, while this illustrates more maleficent pursuits.

📎 Place of torment

The word 'crucible', used to describe a vessel for heating metals to high temperatures, comes from the Latin *crucibulum*, meaning 'little place of torment'.

📎 The futile *Sorcerer*

Though the title of Oscar-winner William Friedkin's 1977 thriller *Sorcerer* is said to have come from a truck that features in the film, it seems strangely fitting for what could be described as a study in futility. Friedkin summed up the plot, which follows four desperate men struggling to transport gallons of volatile nitroglycerine across impossible terrain in order to transform their lives, as 'No matter how much you struggle, you get blown up'.

Commenting on the $21 million production budget, the *New York Times* accused this remake of *The Wages of Fear* (1935) of folly, describing the four protagonists as 'paragons of pointlessly spent money and film time'. Released at the same time as a film that roundly stole its thunder (*Star Wars*), *Sorcerer* proved – as many alchemists did – that it was possible to transform a large pile of money into a small one.

📖 Read

Emsley J. The Shocking History of Phosphorus: A biography of the devil's element. London: Pan Books; 2001.

Morris R. The Last Sorcerers: The path from alchemy to the periodic table. Washington: Joseph Henry Press; 2003.

Wamberg J. Art & Alchemy. Copenhagen: Museum Tusculanum Press; 2006.

📎 Making cold fire

Around 1689, German physician and chemist Hennig Brand (1630–c.1710) began experimenting with a liquid whose golden colour had enticed many fellow alchemists to study it: urine. Brand stored 50 buckets of the liquid until some had evaporated and then boiled and distilled it to create a paste, which he heated for several days. Though his industrious work failed to produce the gold he had hoped for, Brand did end up with a waxy white substance that glowed in the dark and burned while remaining cold.

What Brand named 'cold fire' was the element phosphorus, a key constituent of matches, bombs, fertilisers and toothpaste. Brand demonstrated his luminous discovery to King Charles II and sold the secret of how to manufacture cold fire for the present-day equivalent of around £1000.

LEFT: **German alchemist Hennig Brand discovering phosphorus**
Etching
After Émile Ulm, 19th century
35429i Wellcome Library

RIGHT: **Glass flask used for boiling urine**
Baron Joseph Lister, 1865–77
A629468 Science Museum / L0058254 Wellcome Images

📎 The Baron's urine

Two centuries after Hennig Brand had been busy boiling buckets of urine, antiseptic surgery pioneer Joseph Lister (1827–1912) conducted several experiments on his own golden liquid. Boiling it up in flasks of different shapes, Lister concluded that the urine only decomposed if dust was allowed to enter the flask, thereby supporting the germ-theory of putrefaction.

Meanwhile the urine had been undergoing a change in chemical constitution, as was indicated by an alteration of its colour from a pale straw to a deep amber tint.

Joseph Lister writing in the
British Medical Journal, July 1868

'An Alchemist'

'An Alchemist'
Oil on canvas
After Pieter Bruegel the Elder
RRa0019 / 45122i Wellcome Library

The original 1558 drawing of this cautionary tale by Flemish artist Pieter Bruegel (c.1525–69) set the scene for later satirical depictions of alchemy and has been reproduced in many different graphic forms.

As the preoccupied alchemist drops a coin into a crucible, his despairing wife checks the last of the family's funds and his children play in bare cupboards. The alchemist's assistant, wearing a fool's cap, pumps the fire even though the crucible has toppled away from it. Through the window, the next episode in this sorry scene unfolds, as the destitute family ends up at the poor house.

Full of puff

Alchemists who wasted their time and finances on fruitless activities were scorned as 'puffers', an allusion to the sound of bellows being used to pump their futile fires.

'All crap'

Detail from 'An Alchemist in his Laboratory with his Family'
Engraving
H Cock after Pieter Bruegel
35278i Wellcome Library

In other versions of Bruegel's image, the mysterious man on the right points to the words ALGHE MIST, a phrase that can be translated as 'all crap' or 'everything is lost'.

'A Savant in his Cabinet'

'A Savant in his Cabinet'
Oil on canvas
Mattheus van Helmont, 17th century
RRa0088 / 45123i Wellcome Library

This disordered room, along with the fools on the furnace, gently satirises the alchemist's work.

Nothing more to lose

The first episode of the 2003 Japanese anime series *Fullmetal Alchemist*, based on the manga cartoon of the same name, opens with shots of stirring potions, magical writings and electrical storms. In this alternative present day, alchemy is an advanced and powerful science, but one that comes at a great cost. The narrator sets the scene with the stirring words: 'To create, something of equal value must be lost… My brother and I knew…that gain required sacrifice, that something had to be taken from us, but we thought there was nothing more we could lose…'

Read

McCall T et al. Visual Cultures of Secrecy in Early Modern Europe. Missouri: Truman State University Press; 2013.
Principe L, DeWitt L. Transmutations: Alchemy in art. Philadelphia: Chemical Heritage Foundation; 2002.

'Beware the Greeks bearing gifts'

The Laocoön sculpture standing to the right of this alchemist represents a figure from Roman and Greek mythology. In Virgil's *Aeneid* (19 BCE), Laocoön warns the Trojans about accepting the Greeks' gift of a wooden horse, leading to the idiom 'beware the Greeks bearing gifts'. The story of Laocoön is one of suffering and sacrifice, and its inclusion in this scene could represent a determined spirit struggling when under attack. Alternatively, given the Greek foundations of alchemy, it might also indicate the Trojan-like folly of accepting something too good to be true.

Fools on both sides

Alchemists, and those who seek to benefit from them, have long been satirised. Ben Jonson's (1572–1637) play *The Alchemist*, first performed in 1610, attacks the cheats who prey on gullible fools, but also mocks those whose own greed tempts them to trust in empty promises.

Alchemical furnace

This is one way of transmuting gross compact substances into aereal ones. Another way is by heat. For as fast as the motion of heat can shake off the particles of water from the surface of it: those particles by the said principle will Rote up & down in the air at a distance both from one another & from the particles of air, & make that substance we call vapour.

Isaac Newton (1642–1727), who wrote widely on alchemy, in a letter to Robert Boyle, 1678–79

Alchemical furnace
Stoneware
Germany, 16th–17th century
RRa0026 / A634411 Science Museum /
L0076304 Wellcome Images

Fire and heat were at the core of alchemists' efforts to transform substances, which required the careful control of temperature. For some processes, such as firing ceramics or melting glass, the temperature had to remain constant.

The riddle of the sphinx

The half-human/half-lion sphinx on this furnace could have multiple meanings. It may symbolise the Egyptian heritage of alchemy, the transient state of matter or the elevation of the scholarly human mind above the savage natural world. It might also be a reference to the 'riddle of the sphinx', the brain-twisting question that Oedipus famously solved.

Furnaces
Coloured drawing
15th century
L0032813 Wellcome Images

✐ Firing porcelain

When the ruler of Saxony, Augustus the Strong (1670–1733), heard about the alchemical talents of Johann Friedrich Böttger (1682–1719), he is said to have placed him in 'protective custody' and ordered him to make gold. Böttger failed in his prime mission but did discover 'white gold', the secret of how to make Chinese-style porcelain. The Saxony town of Meissen became the first European centre of porcelain production, a heritage that continues to this day.

Quack with a monkey and clown
Porcelain
Meissen, Germany, 18th century
A78951 Science Museum / L0057352 Wellcome Images

✐ The heat of the furnace

One of John Donne's (1572–1631) bawdier poems, 'Elegy VIII' likens a woman's sex to the heat of the furnace where the alchemist seeks to transform base metal into gold:

> *Then like the chemic's masculine equal fire,*
> *Which in the limbec's warm womb doth inspire*
> *Into th' earth's worthless dirt a soul of gold,*
> *Such cherishing heat her best loved part doth*
> *hold.*

▢ Read

Cheak A. Alchemical Traditions: From antiquity to the avant-garde. Melbourne: Numen Books; 2013.

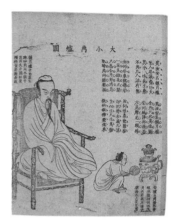

'Great and Small Cauldron and Furnace'
Woodcut
From *Xingming Guizhi* (*Pointers on Spiritual Nature and Bodily Life*)
Yi Zhenren, 1615
L0038973 Wellcome Images

The cauldron and furnace in this illustration refer to symbolic fires within the human head and abdomen. The traditional Chinese practice of inner alchemy, or *neidan*, was based on a complex philosophy that treated the body as a furnace, capable of creating its own life-extending elixir through meditation and breath control.

Swiss–German physician and alchemist Philippus Aureolus Theophrastus Bombast von Hohenheim (1493–1541), more palatably known as Paracelsus, also identified the human body with an alchemical process. He viewed the stomach as a kind of alembic flask, in which food was distilled and the nutritive elements were separated from waste.

Alchemist, physician and astrologer Paracelsus
Engraving
Augustin Hirschvogel after Balthasar Jenichen, 1572
656979i Wellcome Library

Glass flasks

Glass flasks
Europe, 19th century

RR

RRa0101.1–5 / A650263–4, A650223, A650225,
A650228 Science Museum / L0076021 Wellcome Images

The pursuit of alchemy led to the development and refinement of laboratory equipment and processes that are still in use today. One of the most important alchemical techniques was distillation, which isolated a pure liquid from a mixture of fluids by boiling and condensing.

$\wp$

Man then, shall we conclude at length, is the true laboratory of the Hermetic art; his life the subject, the grand distillatory, the thing distilling and the thing distilled, and Self-Knowledge to be at the root of all Alchemical tradition?

M A Atwood in *Hermetic Philosophy and Alchemy*, 1850

📎 Arabic stills

Persian apothecaries are known to have distilled rose water, juniper oil and other herbal medicines in the sixth century, and the swan-necked 'alembic' vessel is referred to in the writings of eighth- and ninth-century Arabic writers.

📖 Read

Al-Khalili J. The House of Wisdom: How Arabic science saved ancient knowledge and gave us the Renaissance. London: Penguin; 2010.

Atwood MA. Hermetic Philosophy and Alchemy: A suggestive inquiry into 'The Hermetic Mystery'. Abingdon: Routledge; 2010.

Rogers A. Proof: The science of booze. New York: Houghton Mifflin; 2014.

Wilson CA. Water of Life: A history of wine-distilling and spirits. Devon: Prospect Books; 2006.

🖉 The legendary Jābir

The bridge between ancient understanding of chemical substances and the development of alchemy in the Muslim world is usually attributed to the eighth-century Arab scholar Jābir ibn Ḥayyān. Yet no one seems very sure which Jābir ibn Ḥayyān to thank for this transmission of knowledge, or even if there was a Jābir ibn Ḥayyān. Possibly born around 720, Jābir – the supposed author of 3000 books – may actually have been a pseudonym for several different authors. When Latin scholars began publishing their own books centuries later, the name Geber emerged. Often thought to be a Latin version of Jābir, it has since transpired Geber was, in fact, a thirteenth-century writer in Latin.

Recreation of a 16th century alchemist's laboratory in the Wellcome Historical Medical Museum
28849i Wellcome Library

'Jābir ibn Ḥayyān Geber'
Engraving
Andre Thevet, 1584
L0005558 Wellcome Images

'Jābir' may be responsible for bringing Chinese lore concerning the element mercury (whose red ore, cinnabar, was used to colour Buddhist temples) to the West. From Aristotelian ideas, he also developed the theory that all metals, and especially valuable gold, could be made by combining appropriate proportions of (shiny) mercury and (yellow) sulphur.

🖉 'Sharp waters'

Islamic physician Abū Bakr Muhammad ibn Zakarīyya al-Rāzī (c.865–925), also known as Rhazes, distilled 'sharp waters' from combinations of vitriol, alum, common salt, saltpetre and ammoniac. These liquids were intended to act as solvents for the base metals alchemists hoped to transform into gold. They were often called elixirs, from the Greek *xerion*, which initially referred simply to a medicine. Later, the idea that these distilled liquids might confer immortality led to a new meaning as the 'water of life'.

Abū Bakr Muhammad ibn Zakarīyya al-Rāzī
Coloured print
S0001954 Wellcome Images

Reproduction of a fifteenth-century Ripley scroll

Reproduction of a 15th-century Ripley scroll
Paper, canvas and wood
Book Works, 2014
RRd0001 / b18597762 Wellcome Library

A reproduction of one of fewer than two dozen copies of a lost fifteenth-century original, this famed alchemical scroll is shrouded in mystery. Despite its name, scholars aren't sure who wrote it or why it was made. Its striking symbolic imagery was also designed to protect its secrets; only the initiated were expected to be able to decode its true meaning.

Several metres long, the scroll fittingly presents the 12 stages of the alchemical process in continuous form. Though the scroll has been in the Wellcome Library since 1924, it has not been on public display since the 1920s.

Golden eagle
From a Ripley scroll
***c*.15th century**
L0031854 Wellcome Images

The golden eagle is thought to represent the chemical process of sublimation, when solid transforms into gas. This might also be interpreted as the human body becoming spirit.

Alchemist holding a flask
From a Ripley scroll
***c*.15th century**
L0032532 Wellcome Images

Depending on your point of view, the alchemist embracing a giant egg-shaped flask in the opening section of the scroll might be the Augustinian monk George Ripley, the legendary Egyptian sage Hermes Trismegistus, Aristotle or God.

Dragon holding a crescent moon
From a Ripley scroll
***c*.15th century**
L0032536 Wellcome Images

A snake or dragon biting its own tail is a common alchemical symbol that is also seen in Islamic art. Known in Greek as the *ouroboros*, its exact meaning was debated between alchemists. At the most basic level, the ouroboros represents a continuous cycle of destruction and recreation, a narrative of sacrifice and resurrection that resonates with the story of Christ's Passion.

*The Birde of Hermes is my name:
eating my winges to make
me tame*

Verse from a Ripley scroll, c.15th century

The alchemical Mr Ripley

George Ripley (c.1415–90) was an Augustinian monk from Yorkshire, who travelled to Europe to further his education in alchemy. While it is unclear if he produced the entire *Ripley Scroll*, the poetic verses that accompany the illustrations on many copies are attributed to him. Despite writing 25 alchemical texts, Ripley reportedly considered the quest for the philosopher's stone to be futile.

For Her Majesty

This copy of the *Ripley Scroll* bears an inscription written in a hand that some have identified as belonging to mathematician and astrologer John Dee (1527–c.1608): 'This long rolle was drawne in colours for me in Lubeck in Germany 1588.' Dee was revered at the court of Queen Elizabeth I, and the painting below shows him combining two elements in front of Elizabeth and Sir Walter Raleigh, among others. When first painted, Dee was shown standing in a circle of human skulls, a symbol of black magic that the artist later painted over.

**John Dee performing an experiment before
Queen Elizabeth I**
Oil on canvas
Henry Gillard Glindoni
47369i Wellcome Library

Read

Cobb C et al. The Chemistry of Alchemy: From dragon's blood to donkey dung, how chemistry was forged. London: Random House; 2014.
Linden SJ. Mystical Metal of Gold: Essays on alchemy and Renaissance culture. New York: AMS; 2007.
Von Kerssenbrock-Krosigk D et al. Art and Alchemy: The mystery of transformation. Düsseldorf: Museum Kunstpalast; 2014.

The allure of alchemy

In his infamous memoir, eighteenth-century libertine Giacomo Casanova (1725–98) describes a visit to the marquise d'Urfé in her castle at Nancy. Madame d'Urfé is a crazy old alchemist, who shows him her alchemical manuscripts. Casanova has brought with him a virgin who he plans to seduce. The seduction is accomplished, with the marquise looking on, she 'wishing to be present at an operation which would result in her own rebirth in nine months' time.'

The Golden Pot

The central character in German author E T A Hoffman's (1776–1822) *Der Goldne Topf (The Golden Pot)*, a novella told in 12 parts, holds a job copying manuscripts in Arabic and 'strange characters'. Hoffmann's story is set in an everyday world where metal comes alive, trees speak and your boss might well be a cursed salamander. It tells the tale of a man who falls in love with a snake and, like an alchemical substance itself, is imprisoned within a 'well-corked crystal bottle, on a shelf in the library'.

Trading in receipts

The buying and selling of alchemical 'receipts', or recipes, was a busy trade in the Early Modern period. Most writers of learned texts collected and traded receipts, an early form of knowledge transfer.

*Let men beware of all books
and receipts that teach the
multiplication of gold or silver
with common quicksilver...for they
cannot be joined inseperably by
any medium, or means whatsoever.*

From Gabriel Plattes's
A Caveat for Alchymists, 17th century

'An Alchemist in his Laboratory'

'An Alchemist in his Laboratory'
Oil on canvas
After David Teniers the Younger, 17th century
RRa0012 / 45088i Wellcome Library

🖉 Cabinets and curiosities

LEFT: **Laboratory and library of an apothecary–physician**
Engraving
Early 17th century
M0007386 Wellcome Images

The rooms of Renaissance alchemists and apothecaries often contained books, curious objects and practical equipment, all side by side. These integrated collections, or 'cabinets', reflect the intertwined nature of looking, thinking, reading and doing.

'An Alchemist in his Laboratory'

'An Alchemist in his Laboratory'
Oil on canvas
A follower of David Teniers the Younger,
17th century
RRa0014 / 47482i Wellcome Library

Flemish artist David Teniers the Younger (1610–90) created over 350 compositions of alchemical scenes, which were much copied. Teniers took a less pejorative approach than Bruegel (see p. 4), depicting the work of honest labourers toiling in their workshops, or of scholars surrounded by books.

📖 Read

Principe L. The Secrets of Alchemy. Chicago: University of Chicago Press; 2013.
Wamberg J. Art & Alchemy. Copenhagen: Museum Tusculanum Press; 2006.

🖋 Alchemical *Metropolis*

In the first feature-length science-fiction film, *Metropolis* (1927), a lone medieval house sits in the midst of the futuristic skyscraper-city. Home to the 'Inventor', the interior is filled with leather-bound books and flasks of boiling liquid. It is also the site of an experiment in eternal life. The Inventor has the stereotypical look of a delusional alchemist; he also uses his artificial life form to spark major change in the city.

'Token Hammers'

'Token Hammers'
Nickel, bronze and ash
John Newling, 2002
RRa0307–11 / L0075857 Wellcome Images

The hammers in John Newling's (b.1952) work
are representative of tools used to transform slugs
of metal into objects with an associated value.
'Token Hammers' incorporates replicas of coin-like
eighteenth- and nineteenth-century tokens that could
be exchanged in order to receive Holy Communion.
This process of striking coins or tokens echoes
the ultimate aim of many alchemists, to turn base
metals into wealth.

The quest to approach that
which is beyond us has been
and continues to be a principal
motivator of humanity.

Artist John Newling in
Currency and Belief, 2003

✒ Financial alchemy

Alchemy has always meant different things to different
people, and in modern parlance the word continues
to be used, not in relation to any scientific or
magical enterprise, but to describe desirable transformations that are often of a creative or financial
nature. It's therefore unsurprising that a number
of venture capital and asset management companies
have taken 'alchemy' for their names.

✒ Self-help alchemy

Paulo Coelho's (b.1947) bestselling 1988 novel *The
Alchemist* has been translated into over 60 languages
and sold more than 20 million copies worldwide. The
book tells the story of an Andalusian shepherd boy
who dreams of finding treasure. He travels and meets

an alchemist who tells him: 'Listen to your heart.' The
New York Times called the book 'more self-help than
literature'.

'An Alchemist'

'An Alchemist'
Oil on canvas
Eugène Lomont, 1890
RRa0039 / 45145i Wellcome Library

By the nineteenth century, alchemy was commonly
depicted in a romantic style that linked it with the
occult. This contemplative alchemist sits alone, having
cast his papers aside, perhaps with a Faustian air of
dissatisfaction.

✒ Selling your soul

German writer Johann Wolfgang von Goethe (1749–
1832) practised alchemy in a laboratory in the attic
of his father's house. He referred to it as 'my veiled
love' and reported being 'very fond of secretly busying
myself in working it out.' In his most famous written
work, an epic poem of the German Faust legend,
a weary scholar dissatisfied with learning from
books is seduced into making a pact with the devil.
In exchange for the scholar's soul, the devil promises
unlimited knowledge and power.

How fortunate are those who can still hope
To rise above this sea of error all around!
For what we need to know is
quite beyond our scope.
And useless all the knowledge
we have found.

Faust in J W Goethe's *Faust, Part I*, 1808

William Gladstone as Dr Faust, making a pact with the devil
Lithograph from *St Stephen's Review*, 1885
564639i Wellcome Library

🖉 The power of coal

One of the earliest and most entertaining doubters of alchemy was Geoffrey Chaucer (1343–1400), who satirised the subject in one of his *Canterbury Tales*, 'The Canon's Yeoman's Tale'. The canon is an alchemist and a conman, whose promise to convert a passing priest's mercury (quicksilver) into silver is achieved by means of a lump of coal that hides the silver. The priest's mercury goes on to the fire, with a dash of the canon's mysterious alchemical powder. With the pretext that the fire needs stoking, the dummy coal is thrown in, and the nugget of silver is revealed. The delighted – and gullible – priest then pays the canon the colossal sum of £40 for the 'secret'.

Chaucer's scientific credentials are sufficient for him to be listed in Elias Ashmole's *Theatrum Chemicum Britannicum* (1652) as one of those 'Famous English Philosophers who have written the Hermetic Mysteries'.

📖 Read

Nummedal T. Alchemy and Authority in the Holy Roman Empire. Chicago: University of Chicago Press; 2007.

🖉 The 'Romance' of alchemy

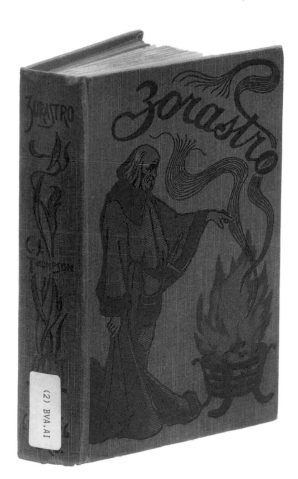

Cover of *Zorastro* by C J S Thompson
1899
b15421855 Wellcome Library

Zorastro was the only novel written by the man who coordinated Henry Wellcome's collecting activities: Charles J Thompson. Billed as 'a Romance', the story is set in sixteenth-century Germany, where Zorastro is a famed healer and alchemist. He believed he had created the elixir of life, but died grasping a vial of it.

Wooden pestles and mortars

Turned and carved mortar
Wood
Europe, 16th–18th century
RRa0100.1a / A658967 Science Museum /
L0076016 Wellcome Images

Turned pestle
Lignum vitae
Europe, 18th–19th century
RRa0100.1b / A28613 Science Museum

Carved mortar and pounder
Wood
18th–19th century
RRa0100.2a–b / A658923, A659417 Science Museum /
L0076018 Wellcome Images

Carved mortar and pestle
Wood
Africa, 19th–early 20th century
RRa0100.3a–b / A658928, A665018 Science Museum /
L0076020 Wellcome Images

Pestles and mortars have been used to break down natural substances and mix preparations for over 12 000 years. Once employed by the ancient Egyptians and Romans, they are a universal symbol of pharmacy, a profession that has its roots in alchemy.

Spagyria

Swiss–German physician Paracelsus (see p. 7) was an outspoken critic of the traditional medicine of Hippocrates and Galen, burned the writings of Avicenna, and advocated alchemy as a method for preparing pharmaceuticals. He invented the word *spagyria*, meaning to draw out and bring together (from the Greek *span* and *ageirein*) and emphasised the analysis and purification of minerals.

...it is not God's design that the remedies should exist for us ready-made, boiled, and salted, but that we should boil them ourselves... Just as flowers grow from the Earth so the remedy grows in the hands of the physician... For the physician's art is like the Earth, which also conceals such potentialities in itself...

Paracelsus, 16th century

Collectors' items

When not being used by keen cooks, pestles and mortars became collectors' items in the early twentieth century, in part because they were no longer needed to compound drug preparations. With the development of its own Tabloid pills (see p. 47), and the machinery to manufacture 600 of them per minute, Burroughs Wellcome & Co. led the pharmaceutical innovations that drove pestles and mortars into museum display cases. Wellcome's own Historical Medical Museum had more than 700 mortars on display when it opened in 1913.

Reconstructed interior of a 17th-century apothecary's shop
Wellcome Historical Medical Museum, 1920s
M0000661 Wellcome Images

Burroughs Wellcome 'Tabloid' products
L0041219 Wellcome Images

Read

Anderson S. Making Medicines: A brief history of pharmacy and pharmaceuticals. London: Pharmaceutical Press; 2005.
Ball P. The Devil's Doctor: Paracelsus and the world of Renaissance magic and science. London: Random House; 2006.

Tabloid table legs

Wellcome table-leg base design
AOC, 2014

The silicon bronze bases at the foot of the tables in the Reading Room are cast in the form of compressed pills, branded with the Wellcome name.

Brockendon pill die
19th century
A600205 Science Museum / L0057808 Wellcome Images

Almost 40 years before Burroughs Wellcome & Co. began manufacturing compressed tablets at its factory in Wandsworth, the painter and inventor William Brockendon (1778–1854) patented this device for 'shaping pills, lozenges and black lead'. Apothecaries and pharmacists who prepared a medical treatment in powder form could use this to compress a measured dose with a hammer, and make a pill.

Medicinal food packaging
19th–20th century

Food

Eating is a social and sensory experience intrinsically linked with health. Greek physician Galen considered knowledge relating to the diet and its effects on health as the most valuable form of medicine. In Galen's view, eating the wrong foods threw the four humours that made up the body out of balance, and illnesses might be treated by ingesting foods with properties opposite to those of the observed symptoms.

While Galen's humoral theory is not part of modern medicine, the importance of eating a balanced diet that responds to the body's dietary needs is still a mainstay of good health. Food provides comfort and sustenance for both the well and the sick, and many foods possess specific medicinal properties, though their benefits may be misunderstood, over-egged or cancelled out by other behaviours. Accepted medical advice on certain foodstuffs can also change, influenced by new scientific research or political motivations.

As the key ingredient in two universal human activities, cooking and eating, food is big business. The industrialisation of food production has delivered year-round access to 'fresh' vegetables that were once considered seasonal; food additives may be used to extend shelf lives; and food manufacturers invest heavily in brand development and marketing campaigns. In some instances, these trade on the perceived health benefits of the products' constituents. These may, of course, not be naturally occurring; they might also fail to deliver what the marketing promises.

> ...some people also eat the flesh of very old donkeys, which is... distasteful as food, like horse and camel meat; which latter meats men who are asinine and camel-like in body and soul also eat!
>
> Galen in *On the Properties of Foodstuffs*, 2nd century CE

Wincarnis showcard

Wincarnis showcard
Cardboard
Coleman & Co., Norwich, 1914–16
RRa0030 / L0075854 Wellcome Images

In the early 1900s, the manufacturers of Wincarnis, a fortified wine sold as a restorative tonic, employed 'Nurse Wincarnis' as part of their £50 000-a-year marketing efforts. Besides this beckoning showcard, the nurse gave 'Little Lectures' in newspapers and appeared in other advertisements extolling the drink's invigorating properties and offering opportunities for 'a liberal free trial'. The company also provided free samples to doctors, 10 000 of whom wrote recommendations for the product – or so the manufacturers claimed.

At the time, Wincarnis was made to a secret recipe combining port wine, malt extract and Liebig's Extract of Meat. Advertisements emphasised the nutritional value of these added ingredients, even though they amounted to only 1 or 2 per cent of a drink that contained almost 20 per cent alcohol.

Liebig's Beef Wine advertisement
S Stephens & Liebig's Meat Company
b16556859 Wellcome Library

[The advertisement] is calculated to make people think it is really a nutritious mixture, and when we come to the analysis we find that the little amount of meat extract is nothing approaching the amount of an ordinary cup of beef-tea. My point is the misleading influence of the advertisements.

Dr Mary Sturge, referring to Wincarnis while giving evidence to the House of Commons Select Committee on Patent Medicines, 1912

Supporting the troops

In 1914, Wincarnis manufacturers Coleman & Co. issued a booklet for troops at the front called 'What You Want to Say and How to Say it in French'. The company's wartime Wincarnis advertisements targeted soldiers, offering help 'when your nerves are "on edge"'.

No more beef

Today, Wincarnis is made from wine and malt extract with a panoply of added herbs and spices. Instead of beef extract, the new formula contains 'gentian root, mugwort, angelica root, balm mint, fennel seed, coriander seed, peppermint leaves, cardamom seeds and cassia bark'.

Doses of iron filings and iodine

In 4000 BCE, Persian physician Melampus put iron into a soldier's wine for ten days in order to cure his impotence. This early example of adding nutrients to food in order to address a deficiency was embraced on a much larger scale in the 1900s, when iodine was first added to table salt in an effort to reduce the incidence of goitre. Milk fortified with vitamin D and cereals with added thiamin, niacin, riboflavin and iron followed.

Woman with large goitre
Watercolour drawing
Thomas Godart, 1881
L0061670 Wellcome Images

As a public-health strategy, fortification allows for rapid interventions without requiring people to change their eating habits. However, it can also be used by manufacturers to imbue foods that have little nutritional value with a healthy appeal.

Read

Nestle M. Food Politics: How the food industry influences nutrition and health. Berkeley: University of California Press; 2013.

Paregoric Elixir bottle

Paregoric Elixir bottle
Glass
N Wood & Son, Maine, 1843–87
RRa0298 / L0075845 Wellcome Images

Paregoric is a tincture of opium and camphor, which was dropped and dissolved in water before being drunk. First used by Dutch chemist Jakob Le Mort (1650–1718) to treat asthma, its ability to suppress coughs made it a popular treatment for tuberculosis.

...[Paregoric Elixir] excellently allays the tickling, which provokes frequent coughing; and yet at the same time opens the breast, and gives greater liberty of breathing: the opium procures a temporary relief from the symptoms, whilst the other ingredients tend to remove the cause, and prevent their return. It is given to children against the chin-cough...

From John Quincy's *Pharmacopœia Officinalis & Extemporanea: Or a complete English dispensatory*, 1782

🗍 Read

Jackson M. Allergy: The history of a modern malady. London: Reaktion Books; 2006.
Wilson B. Swindled: From poison sweets to counterfeit coffee – the dark history of the food cheats. London: John Murray; 2008.

Hall's Coca Wine advertisement
Stephen Smith & Co., *c*.1916
b1558432x Wellcome Library

One of several competitors to Wincarnis, Hall's Coca Wine contained cocaine. It was promoted as an invigorating tonic and was endorsed by the medical profession.

Japanese Vigor Tonic packaging

Japanese Vigor Tonic packaging
Cardboard
J H Hart, England, *c*.1920
RRa0299 / L0075847–8 Wellcome Images

Gum Tragacantha bottle

Gum Tragacantha bottle
Glass
Merck, Darmstadt, 1930
RRa0296 / L0075844 Wellcome Images

Once known as gum dragon, gum tragacanth oozes out of the root of the tragacanth, or goat's horn, plant.

Gum Dragon is of a glutinous Nature, good to correct the Acrimony and Sharpness of the Humours, and therefore pectoral and good for Coughs, Hoarseness, and catarrhous Defluxions... Outwardly it is good in Collyriums for hot inflamed eyes.

From Joseph Miller's *Botanicum Officinale; Or a compendious Herbal*, 1722

✐ Burger attack

In 1978, a 35-year-old Montreal woman suffered what a letter to the *New England Journal of Medicine* described as a 'life-threatening attack' after taking a few bites of a hamburger from a well-known fast-food chain. Her face, body and arms swelled up, she experienced stomach pains and found it difficult to breath. When scientists at the city's McGill University analysed her meal, they identified the problem: the woman had suffered an unusual allergic reaction to gum tragacanth, which had been used as a thickener in the burger sauce.

Dr Fowler's Meat and Malt Tonic bottle

Dr Fowler's Meat and Malt Tonic bottle
Glass
America, late 19th century
RRa0297 / L0076144–5 Wellcome Images

Promoted with the slogan 'Here's the beef!', Dr Fowler's Meat and Malt Tonic was, like Bovril, a meat extract similar to that first developed and promoted by the celebrated chemist Baron Justus von Liebig (1803–73). The original Liebig's Extract, a combination of reduced meat stock and salt, was a molasses-like black spread; it required three kilograms of meat to make 100g of extract.

As my experiments include the changes which flesh undergoes in its preparation for food, I trust that not only physiologists and chemists, but also the lovers of a rational system of diet, will find in the following pages many observations worthy of their attention.

Dr Justus von Liebig in the preface to *Researches on the Chemistry of Food*, 1847

Bovril jars

Bovril jars
Amber-brown glass
Bovril Ltd., c.1930s
RRa0293 / L0075841 Wellcome Images

Bovril beef extract was developed by Scottish butcher-turned-entrepreneur John Lawston Johnston (1839–1900) after he won a contract to supply beef to the French army in the 1870s. Johnston believed his 'fluid beef' was superior to similar products thanks to the addition of finely ground lean meat. In one advertisement in 1889, he offered a thousand guineas to anyone who could disprove the statement that one ounce of Bovril contained 'more real and direct nourishment' than 50 ounces of the market leader at the time, Liebig's Extract.

The name Johnston gave to what was essentially an industrially concentrated beef tea (see p. 34) is a portmanteau of the words 'bovine' and 'vril', a life-giving substance mentioned in an early science-fiction novel. Bovril was so successful that within ten years of the first jar coming off the production line, Johnston had sold the company for £2 million.

These subterranean philosophers assert that by one operation of vril, which Faraday would perhaps call 'atmospheric magnetism', they can influence...the weather; that by operations akin to those ascribed to mesmerism, electrobiology, odic force, &c., but applied scientifically through vril conductors, they can exercise influence over minds, and bodies animal and vegetable...

From Edward Bulwer-Lytton's *Vril: The power of the coming race*, 1871

Bovril Cordial bottle

Bovril Cordial bottle
Amber-brown glass
Bovril (Canada) Ltd., 1940–50
RRa0292 / L0075840 Wellcome Images

Described as 'nutritious, invigorating & delicious', a teaspoonful of Bovril cordial dissolved in a cup of boiling water was recommended for 'refreshing sleep'. The label on this bottle pictures Hercules killing the Nemean lion. This emphasis on power and strength, a recurring theme in Bovril advertising, was unusual for the time and set the company's products apart from other foods.

Fighting off legions

A belief in the energy-giving power of magic potions is encouraged by numerous children's stories, notably René Goscinny (1926–77) and Albert Uderzo's (b.1927) *Asterix the Gaul* series. Set around 50 BCE, the French comic books tell the tales of the idiosyncratic inhabitants of a small village resisting the onslaught of Julius Caesar and his army. When the eponymous hero takes a swig of a secret potion, he has – for a limited time – so much energy and strength he can fight off legions of Romans.

As might be expected from its French provenance, food also plays a key role in the books; on the final page of every adventure Asterix and his fellow villagers relax over a sumptuous feast.

IS LIQUID LIFE.

'Bovril is Liquid Life'
From an advertisement in Abel Heywood and
Son's *Influenza: Its cause, cure and prevention*,
1902
b1019986x Wellcome Library

The drink of popes and strong men

An early proponent of celebrity 'endorsements', Bovril may be the only health drink ever to have been linked to the Pope. In the 1890s, Bovril issued an advertisement showing the Pope holding a mug of Bovril under the line 'The two infallible powers: The Pope & Bovril'. Around the same time, explorer Henry Morton Stanley (1841–1904) lent his name to the product, which was advertised with the phrase, 'Stanley recruits his strength with Bovril'. Rudyard Kipling (1865–1936) was also happy to praise Bovril in public, as was Eugen Sandow (1867–1925), known as the 'Strongest Man in the World'.

Bovril promotional parrots

'A New Sandow Pose'
Photograph
From *Sandow's Magazine
of Physical Culture*, 1902
Eugen Sandow
b13519475 Wellcome Library

Bovril promotional parrots
Paper
Bovril, *c.*1930s
RRa0301–2 / L0075850–1 Wellcome Images

These Amazonian parrots may be a reference to the source of much of Bovril's beef: South America. In the Entre Rios region in Argentina, where the company once owned half a million hectares of land and 1.5 million cattle, there is still a town called Bovril.

A cup winner

Before the days of super-stadiums and corporate hospitality, a cup of warming Bovril was a familiar half-time treat for football fans standing on the terraces. But Bovril was also the first commercial organisation to be linked with an association football club. In 1898, an advertisement titled 'Bovril Wins' quoted FA Cup winners Nottingham Forest, stating '…we used BOVRIL very freely. We consider it was A VERY IMPORTANT FACTOR in giving our men strength and staying power.'

Numol Body Builder jar

Gevral bottles

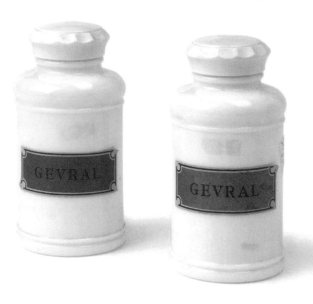

Numol Body Builder jar
Ceramic
Numol, 20th century
RRa0300 / L0075849 Wellcome Images

This jar is emblazoned with the phrase 'Lecithin Food', a reference to the naturally occurring substance lecithin, which can be found in soy beans, sunflower seeds and egg yolk. Non-toxic, with a wide range of applications, lecithin is frequently added to powdered food to make it dissolve more easily, to margarine to improve its spreadability, or to chocolate to reduce the amount of costly cocoa butter content.

Lecithin is also a major constituent of human cell membranes, which leads to claims that it should be taken as a food supplement. However, lecithin is produced naturally by a healthy liver and, if consumed, is broken down in the intestine before most of it has a chance to reach the body's tissues.

Gevral bottles
Glass and plastic
Lederle Laboratories, American Cyanamid Co., 1960–70
RRa0295 / L0075843 Wellcome Images

Each of the 100 capsules in one of these bottles was packed with 14 vitamins and 11 minerals. Gevral's 'vitamin-mineral-nutritional' dietary supplements were marketed 'for the entire family'.

Receiving 'full benefit'

As New York Commissioner of Health, Ernst J Lederle (1865–1921) organised the vaccination of 800 000 people during an epidemic of smallpox and promoted the pasteurisation of milk to prevent the spread of tuberculosis. After he fell out of favour with local politicians in 1903, he formed Lederle Laboratories for 'chemical, bacteriological and sanitary analysis'. The company went on to manufacture vaccines, vitamins, antibiotics and sterile blood plasma.

In 1949, Lederle Laboratories developed a process for manufacturing soft gelatin capsules filled with dry powders or liquids. This promised, so the marketing claimed, 'better absorption and relative freedom from unpleasant aftertaste', ensuring patients received 'the full benefit from the potency'.

The Stark diet

In 1769, British physician William Stark (1740–70) set out to complete 24 experiments to prove his hypothesis that 'a pleasant and varied diet was as healthful as simpler stricter diets'. Testing his theory on himself, he started by eating only bread, water and sugar for a month. He then added new foods to his diet, one at a time, from olive oil and milk to roast goose and boiled beef. As Stark tried eating only puddings, he started to show signs of scurvy. He then moved on to meals consisting solely of Cheshire cheese. And then, before he could reach the experiments involving fruits and vegetables, he died, presumably as a consequence of his vitamin C-deficient diet.

Vital amines

Polish-born biochemist Casimir Funk (1884–1967) was the first to name the active factor in brown rice, which had been observed in 1890s Java to prevent rickets, a disease much more prevalent in those fed on a diet of polished white rice. Funk mistakenly thought he had isolated the vital factor, which he identified as a type of chemical called an 'amine'. He named his 'discovery' vitamine in 1912. When later research showed that other trace nutrients were not amines, the term was shortened to vitamin.

Vitacal Tablets box

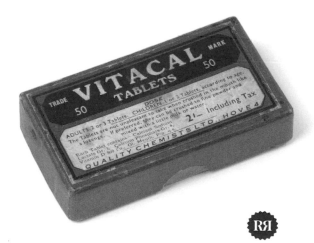

Vitacal Tablets box
Cardboard
Quality Chemists Ltd., Hove, 20th century
RRa0305 / L0075855 Wellcome Images

Gramenose tin

FOOD

Gramenose tin
Tin
Etablissements Jammet, Paris, c.1920
RRa0291 / L0075836–7 Wellcome Images

This tin once contained a finely-ground flour mixed with grains, nuts, seeds and other vegetables. Offering a variety of nutritional benefits, its manufacturers produced promotional postcards that harked back to traditional country life in France.

Read

Frankenburg R. Vitamin Discoveries and Disasters: History, science, and controversies. Santa Barbara: Greenwood Publishing; 2009.
Harvie DI. Limeys: The conquest of scurvy. Stroud: Sutton Publishing; 2005.

OSR Vegetable Tablets box

OSR Vegetable Tablets box
Standard Remedy Co., Baltimore,
20th century
RRa0312 / L0075860 Wellcome Images

These laxative tablets include aloes, rhubarb, podo-phyllum, senna, capsicum, spearmint, pennyroyal and red clover.

Removing bad blood

James Morison's 'Vegetable Universal Pills' were designed to purge the body of bad blood, which their inventor considered responsible for all disease. Businessman Morison (1770–1840) produced the remedy – along with his own philosophy of medicine – after consulting multiple physicians about his own ill health. When none could cure him, he embarked on both a business venture and a crusade against established medical science.

Morison set up the 'British College of Health', called himself 'the Hygeist' and published the *Hygeian Journal*. Termed the 'King of Quacks' by the editor of the *Lancet*, he also suggested his pills could be taken in large quantities – up to 30 tablets a day. Morison made a fortune, despite damning media reports, which he always took to court.

We may safely claim the merit of having crushed the self-styled hygeist system of wholesale poisoning, since we commenced exposing the homicidal tricks of these impudent and ignorant scamps...[whose pills] composed of nothing more than gamboge and aloes.

The proprietors of the *Weekly Dispatch* giving evidence at their trial for libel (of which they were acquitted), 1837

Sprouting vegetables as a result of taking James Morison's vegetable pills
Coloured lithograph
C J Grant, 1831
11852i Wellcome Library

Quackery

Though contemporary definitions treat quacks as people dishonestly claiming specialist knowledge or operating outside orthodox medicine, before the twentieth century the word simply referred to an individual practising medicine for commercial gain. Derived from the Dutch *quacksalver*, the term originally described an itinerant pedlar 'quacking' about his wares.

Quack doctor selling remedies from his caravan
Chromolithograph
Tom Merry, 1889
13793i Wellcome Library

Most quacks lacked medical qualifications and built up sales of their secret-formula nostrums by virtue of published testimonials. Commonly depicted as rogues, some did, however, have formal medical training and many sold remedies lifted from well-established guides to medicinal plants. Some were also careful not to make any personal claims for their products, leaving the marketing-speak to their satisfied customers.

At the same time, members of the established medical profession also engaged in activities that, for some, might be described as 'quackery'. Hans Sloan promoted medicinal chocolate and vaccination pioneer Edward Jenners's method for purifying emetic tartar was used to treat a variety of complaints.

There is scarcely a man of any medical eminence whose name has not, by direct assertion or by implication, been connected with some kill-or-cure specific... But what is the culpability of him who vends his pleasant but noxious beverage under its true character, compared with his who takes advantage of his character as a guardian of the public health, to palm off Godfrey's Cordial and other poisons on the credulous and unwary?

'Quack Medicines' in the *Spectator*, 1845

....

⌀ Charlatans

Like quacks, seventeenth-century charlatans were itinerant sellers of remedies. Deriving from the Italian verb *ciarlare*, the word refers to their babbling sales style.

....

⌀ Tono-Bungay

When the conflicted protagonist of H G Wells's (1866–1946) novel *Tono-Bungay* needs to secure a healthy salary in order to woo his beloved, he joins forces with his uncle, a pharmacist selling what they both know to be a useless patent remedy. Despite bringing him wealth, influence and respect, the 'hero' of the book ultimately considers the Tono-Bungay business to be 'One vast dismal spectacle of witless waste!'. Depicting the demise of rigidly hierarchical Victorian society, the book also explores tensions between the search for scientific truth and the need for human fulfilment.

We set upon this bright enterprise of selling slightly injurious rubbish at one-and-three-halfpence... That alluring, button-holeing, let-me-just-tell-you-something-you-ought-to-know style of newspaper advertisement, with every now and then a convulsive jump of some attractive phrase into capitals... 'HILARITY – TONO-BUNGAY. Like Mountain Air in the Veins'. The penetrating trio of questions: 'Are you bored with your Business? Are you bored with your Dinner? Are you bored with your Wife?'

From H G Wells's *Tono-Bungay*, 1909

'A Quack in the Right Place'
Wood engraving
From *Punch*, December 1864
C J
b1312142x Wellcome Library

📎 The virtues of vegetables

In the 1970s, bifurcated anthropomorphic carrots appeared regularly on the BBC television programme *That's Life*, especially when their two forks were hilariously joined by a smaller third growth in the middle. Similarly shaped mandrakes, used in medieval medicine as an emetic and to bathe ulcers, were believed to shriek when pulled from the earth.

The appearance of edible plants was once linked to their use in medicine. Red chillis were recommended to restore colour to the cheeks, and stems of asparagus were the Renaissance Viagra. They were also prescribed for relieving pain when urinating. The pomegranate bursts with seeds, linking its use with the fertilised womb.

MANHOOD:

How Lost, by Acquired Diseases ;

How Regained, by Vegetable Compounds.

IN presenting this little book, I am actuated by the following reason : Because the great number of cases continually coming under my notice, without being solicited, convinces me of the number who must be suffering in solitude, and this book will at least enable the sufferer, by a proper description of symptoms and simple mode of treatment, to either relieve himself, or obtain that attention which the mistaken policy of the profession has hitherto denied him.

From *A Brief Treatise on Venereal Disease and Spermatorrhoea*, 20th century
S Gould
L0024120 Wellcome Images

Dinner should be taken in summer soon before sunset and consist of bread, vegetables, and barley cake. One will start with raw vegetables, with the exception of cucumber and horseradish, for these are vegetables that should be eaten toward the end of the meal.

From the diary of 4th-century BCE physician Diocles of Carystus, as reported by Oribasius

Being encouraged to eat linseed
From *Yinshan Zhengyao* (*Principles of Correct Diet*), 1368–1644
Hu Shihui
L0034695 Wellcome Images

This distinguished gentleman is being encouraged to eat linseed in the dry autumn, in order to restore moisture to the body.

📖 Read

Freedman PH. Food: The history of taste. London: Thames & Hudson; 2007.

Gratzer W. Terrors of the Table: The curious history of nutrition. New York: Oxford University Press; 2005.

Porter R. Quacks: Fakers & charlatans in English medicine. Stroud: Tempus Publishing; 2000.

Cups, boats and warmers for feeding infants and invalids

Posset pot
Tin-glazed earthenware
1670–1760
RRa0102.3 / A634389 Science Museum / L0076029 Wellcome Images

Possets were custard-like dishes prepared for the sick and often taken as a restorative after childbirth. Typical ingredients in the seventeenth and eighteenth centuries included eggs, cream, sugar, wine or brandy, nutmeg, cinnamon and lemon. Bread or biscuits might also be added.

There is no doubt that the period of convalescence may be much shortened by the wise administration of food, and that the subsequent health of the patient may be either made or marred by the action of the nurse in this respect.

From Mary A Boland's *Handbook of Invalid Cooking: For the use of nurses*, 1898

A convalescing man eating a meal
Coloured etching
James Gillray after John Sneyd, 1804
12050i Wellcome Library

Jewish penicillin

The supposed curative properties of chicken soup have a surprisingly long history. The rabbi and physician Moses Maimonides (1135–1204) produced ten health guides for the nephew of Saladin, the first sultan of Egypt, as well as many writings on the interpretation of the scriptures. His advice – on eating, sleeping, weekly baths, sex and more – stands up well today. He invokes the Book of Leviticus when it is convenient, using it to back up already sound medical arguments, such as that overeating leads to poor digestion. In general, Maimonides was less worried about categories of allowed or prohibited foods than he was about the right amounts to eat:

'As long as a person works and takes plenty of exercise, does not eat to satiety, and his bowels are regular, no ailment will befall him and his strength keeps developing, even if he eat unwholesome food.'

According to Maimonides, chicken soup serves to 'neutralise bodily constitution'. He claims it may be effective in treating diseases from leprosy to asthma. Recent clinical studies have shown that the soup contains proteins and other substances that may have beneficial decongestant and anti-inflammatory effects. But the nostalgic recall that it provokes of the childhood home may be just as important. That, and the irresistible – to vegetarians, at least – aroma and taste.

Pap boat

Pap boat
Glazed earthenware
1701–1900
RRa0102.8 / A62854 Science Museum /
L0076039 Wellcome Images

Pap boats were used to administer a gruel of milk and water, which may also have included bread, egg and sometimes wine or beer. Vessels intended for infants were often attractively decorated, as seen with this bird design.

Feeding pap to infants in the eighteenth century was controversial. Some advocated it as an acceptable replacement for milk, others disagreed; there were also concerns that children were being overfed. When pap eventually went out of fashion, manufacturers rebranded pap boats as invalid feeders.

Advertisement for Mellin's food for infants and invalids
Photogravure
1897
571264i Wellcome Library

English chemist Gustav Mellin's 'milk modifier' was mixed with milk and water in order, so the company reported, to remove the 'tough, indigestible curds in the stomach so trying to the infant digestion'.

This was the same technique used by Imperial Granum Food for babies, which was also marketed as a 'salvator for invalids'.

Imperial Granum box

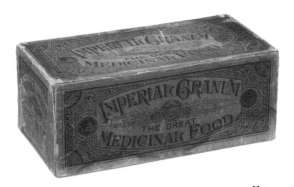

Imperial Granum box
Cardboard
c.1877
RRa0303 / L0075853 Wellcome Images

Trade card promoting 'Sugar of Milk'
Wells, Richardson & Co., 1890s
L0034387 Wellcome Images

'Sugar of Milk', this card states, is the principal element of both 'Lactated Food' and 'Mother's Milk'. Quoting an unnamed 'prominent physician', it suggests that the general use of Lactated Food could reduce the 'prevalent' infant death rate.

Broken feeding bottle

Broken feeding bottle
Glazed earthenware
Rouen, 1730–1830
RRa0102.7 / A89207 Science Museum /
L0076037 Wellcome Images

Feeding cup

Feeding cup
Glazed earthenware
1751–1850
RRa0102.11 / A625716 Science Museum /
L0076049 Wellcome Images

The pot is somewhat in the form
of an urn; its handle and neck
or spout are not unlike those of
a coffee pot except that the neck
of this arises from the very bottom
of the pot and is very small... The
end of the spout is a little raised
and forms a roundish knob...

Physician Hugh Smith describing his 'bubby-
pot' in *Letters to Married Women on Nursing
and the Management of Children*, 1772

Glencliff Premium Vitamin Milk bottle

FOOD

Glencliff Premium Vitamin Milk bottle
Duraglass
Glencliff, 1950–65
RRa0294 / L0075842 Wellcome Images

This 'premium' Glencliff milk contains vitamins A,
B1 and B2, niacin, iron and iodine. The company's
marketing stressed the milk's quality and freshness,
as well as the fact that there was 'always a dealer
near you'.

Read

Apple RD. Mothers and Medicine: A social history
of infant feeding, 1890–1950. Madison: University of Wisconsin Press; 1987.
Wolf JH. Don't Kill Your Baby: Public health and
the decline of breastfeeding in the 19th and
20th centuries. Columbus: Ohio State University
Press; 2001.

Invalid feeding cup

Invalid feeding cup
Polychrome majolica
Europe, 1701–1850
RRa0102.6 / A625588 Science Museum /
L0076035 Wellcome Images

Beef tea

Made by boiling beef in water, warm beef tea was
commonly fed to invalids unable to take other food.

> *Have we, as physicians, really
> any scientific knowledge at all
> concerning the actual nutritive
> power of this beef-tea, in the
> fabrication of which, as we have
> said, in one hospital alone in
> London, some 52 000 pounds
> of meat are annually consumed?*
>
> *British Medical Journal, Vol. 1,* 1865

Invalid feeding cup

Invalid feeding cup
Glazed earthenware
England
RRa0102.1 / A608300 Science Museum /
L0076024 Wellcome Images

> *In sending dishes or preparations
> up to invalids, let everything look
> as tempting as possible. Have a
> clean tray-cloth laid smoothly over
> the tray; let the spoons, tumblers,
> cups and saucers etc. be very
> clean and bright. Gruel served
> in a tumbler is more appetizing
> than when served in a basin
> of cup and saucer.*
>
> From Isabella Beeton's *Beeton's Book
> of Household Management,* 1861

Nursing in the home

Up until the end of the eighteenth century, most
nursing took place in the home, making, as Florence
Nightingale (1820–1910) posited, every woman a
nurse. When the sick and needy began to be offered
health care within hospitals, infirmaries and asylums,
the job of a nurse was more domestic than medical.
Nurses had no training, provided little care and
were popularly (if not always fairly) characterised
as morally dubious drunks.

**A hired nurse in a dead sleep after a drop
of comfort**
Etching with watercolour
Thomas Rowlandson, 1807
11876i Wellcome Library

In novels, lives are saved by 'strong jelly!' (what does strong jelly mean?) and by other things equally absurd.

Florence Nightingale in *Notes On Nursing: What it is and what it is not*, 1860

'Strong jelly!'

In her 1860 book *Notes On Nursing: What it is and what it is not*, Florence Nightingale takes exception to the use of jelly:

> *'Jelly is another article of diet in great favour with nurses and friends of the sick; even if it could be eaten solid, it would not nourish, but it is simply the height of folly to…make it into a certain bulk by dissolving it in water and then to give it to the sick, as if the mere bulk represented nourishment. It is now known that jelly does not nourish, that it has a tendency to produce diarrhoea, – and to trust to it to repair the waste of a diseased constitution is simply to starve the sick under the guise of feeding them.'*

Mrs Gamp proved to be very choice in her eating, and repudiated hashed mutton with scorn. In her drinking too, she was very punctual and particular, requiring a pint of mild porter at lunch, a pint at dinner, half-a-pint as a species of stay or holdfast between dinner and tea, and a pint of the celebrated staggering ale, or Real Old Brighton Tipper, at supper; besides the bottle on the chimneypiece, and such casual invitations to refresh herself with wine as the good breeding of her employers might prompt them to offer.

Charles Dickens describing the nurse and midwife Sarah Gamp in *Martin Chuzzlewit*, 1843–44

FOOD

Food, sensuality and death

The healing power of food has been a popular subject for films, where it is often employed as a metaphor for sensual liberation. In *Babette's Feast* (1987), the family of a Lutheran pastor in nineteenth-century Denmark takes in a young French refugee who gradually instructs them in the delights of good food. A similar arrivée brings conflict and pleasure in *Chocolat* (2000), when she opens a chocolaterie during Lent. *Big Night* (1996), a film about Italian brothers struggling to open a restaurant in America, sees all ills put right by the simple cooking – shown in real time – of an omelette.

In *La Grande Bouffe* (1973), four middle-aged men meet at a house where they plan to gorge themselves to death. In the final scene, the survivor is seen feasting on a huge blancmange shaped like the breasts that made his first meal.

'An Exquisite Taste'
Aquatint with watercolour
George Hunt, 1831
10511i Wellcome Library

Food warmer

Food warmer
Glazed earthenware
Europe, 1780–1820
RRa0102.12 / A608441 Science Museum / L0076052
Wellcome Images

This double-boiler system incorporates space for an oil lamp and a water bath to warm the jug placed above it.

The Maillard reaction

In the 1910s, the French physician and chemist Louis Camille Maillard (1878–1936) described the process of browning food, which generates pleasant aromatic flavours. The mechanism that takes his name is a reaction between amino acids and reducing sugars that usually takes place when food is heated to around 154°C.

'Mangia Maccaroni' ('Eating Macaroni')
Hand-coloured lithograph
Gatti and Dura
30359i Wellcome Library

Pre-human cooking

Some scientists believe cooking existed before *Homo sapiens* did. In his 2009 book *Catching Fire*, Professor Richard Wrangham sets out his theory that 'the transformative moment that gave rise to the genus *Homo*, one of the great transitions in the history of life, stemmed from the control of fire and the advent of cooked meals'.

Read

Allen JS. The Omnivorous Mind: Our evolving relationship with food. Cambridge: Harvard University Press; 2012.

Gilman SL. Obesity: The biography. New York: Oxford University Press; 2010.

Lebesco K, Laccarato P. Edible Ideologies: Representing food and meaning. Albany: State University of New York Press; 2008.

Toussaint-Samat M. A History of Food. Chichester: Wiley; 2009.

Wrangham R. Catching Fire: How cooking made us human. London: Profile; 2009.

✐ Writing recipes

For many centuries, personal collections of old recipes and remedies have been passed down from one generation to the next, leading to an accumulation of knowledge within families. To modern scholars, these documents reveal the practical sciences and mechanical arts practised by women, who were responsible for the sustenance and health of their families. They also provide insights into the health problems of the time.

The oldest European artefact in the Wellcome Library is a list of old English folk remedies, which dates back to 1000; the first book officially registered as an acquisition for the Library is a seventeenth-century book of 'receipts' for medicinal remedies.

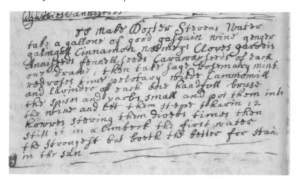

'To make Doctor Stevens water'
From *Book of Receipts, Cooking, Medical & Veterinary*, 1688–1727
Meade [& others]
b1951275 Wellcome Library

✐ On the morals of cookery books

In 1923 author Joseph Conrad (1857–1924) took a break from his own work on *The Secret Agent* to write the preface to his wife Jessie's *Handbook of Cookery for a Small House*. Referring to cooking as 'a moral agent', he wrote:

> 'Of all the books produced since the most remote ages by human talents and industry those only that treat of cooking are, from a moral point of view, above suspicion. The intention of every other piece of prose may be discussed and even mistrusted; but the purpose of a cookery book is one and unmistakable. Its object can conceivably be no other than to increase the happiness of mankind.'

Boil a mouse in urine and pound wythe chopped acorn and see coal and feed to childe on empty gull.

'Cure for bed wetting' in Grace Acton's recipe collection, 1621

🗋 Read

Beeton I. Beeton's Household Management. Oxford: Oxford University Press; 2000.
Nightingale F. On Nursing: What it is and what it is not. Glasgow: Blackie & Son Ltd.; 1974.
Powell O. Galen: On the properties of foodstuffs. Cambridge: Cambridge University Press; 2003.

Pewter feeding cups

Pewter feeding cups
18th century
RRa0102.9, RRa0102.2 / A625596, A625595 Science Museum / L0076041 Wellcome Images

Ceramic feeding cups

Ceramic feeding cups
England, 1880–1920
RRa0102.4–5 / 1983-1407/5, 1983-1407/7 Science Museum / L0076050, L0076052 Wellcome Images

FOOD

Aëdes aegypti
Grace Edwards, 1914

Travel

People, goods, knowledge and disease all travel – sometimes intentionally, sometimes by accident. These global movements can lead to deliberate, surprising and sometimes catastrophic consequences.

Travel is synonymous with broadening the mind, but encountering 'different' people, cultures and biological environments can also feed fear of 'the other'. The 'outbreak narrative', a common theme in popular culture, draws on an extreme version of this: the terror of a species-threatening event caused by clashing ecosystems. In fact, the best outbreak stories tell tales of conflicting social and political frameworks as much as unexpected killer diseases, even if they are propped up by scientific paraphernalia such as microscopes and epidemiological maps.

In reality, despite the major twentieth-century medical advances of antibiotics and effective public-health measures, most infectious diseases have not been eradicated. Large populations, sedentary living in crowded urban areas and vast and rapid transportation systems are all contributing factors to the spread of disease. The evolutionary adaptations of bacteria, viruses and their vectors, which refuse to recognise human geographical boundaries, are also to blame. As anti-microbial resistance mechanisms spread internationally, the world may end up in what the World Health Organization calls 'a post-antibiotic era'.

One of the biggest global health stories of modern times is undoubtedly HIV and AIDS, a phenomenon that took the medical world by surprise and travelled at what was then unprecedented speed. Like other deadly contagious diseases, HIV quickly acquired an associated stigma. This has made it difficult to control, in spite of major investments in education programmes and drug development.

...this was all my provision, and threw me into terrible agonies of mind, that for a while I [ran] about like a Mad-man; Night coming upon me, I began with a heavy Heart to consider what would be my Lot if there were ravenous Beasts in that Country, seeing at Night they always come aboard for their Prey.

From Daniel Defoe's *The Life and Strange Surprising Adventures of Robinson Crusoe*, 1719

Over-sized models of invertebrates that transmit disease

Aëdes aegypti – yellow-fever mosquito
Wax
Grace Edwards, 1914
RRa0313 / L0075807 Wellcome Images

Invertebrates are common transmitters, or vectors, of disease. The *Aëdes aegypti* mosquito spreads dengue fever, chikungunya and yellow fever, a virus affecting 200 000 people each year and causing 30 000 annual deaths. Despite the availability of a vaccine, these numbers are on the rise, particularly in West Africa.

'Yellow Fever in Buenos Aires'

'Yellow Fever in Buenos Aires'
Oil on canvas
Juan Manuel Blanes, 1871
RRa0314 / 525072i Wellcome Library

This dramatic scene depicts just one of the thousands of deaths caused by an outbreak of yellow fever in Buenos Aires during the first four months of 1871. The *Lancet* described the mortality figures – officially reported as 13 402 – as 'sufficiently large to sate the most rapacious appetite for horrors'.

At the time, yellow fever was thought to be contagious, and the Buenos Aires epidemic was blamed on passengers arriving by sea. The *Buenos Aires Standard* pointed the finger at a ship captain who threw the dead bodies of 14 fever victims overboard. He also omitted to tell port officials that he had stopped off in Barcelona (where the vessel picked up the disease) en route from Genoa, thereby allowing his cargo of infected immigrants to spread into the unsuspecting city.

...in March the pestilence spread with frightful rapidity, and...the greatest terror prevailed in all quarters of the town. The press endeavoured to calm the fears of the inhabitants by publishing fewer deaths than took place... nothing could exceed the gloom and desolation that pervaded the city...

Dr J H Scrivener writing about the 1871 epidemic in the *Medical Times and Gazette*, 1872

Transatlantic disease trade

The timing of yellow-fever epidemics in the Americas suggests the disease first travelled across the Atlantic in the early sixteenth century; *Aëdes aegypti* mosquitoes were inadvertently transported from Africa in the bilges of transatlantic slave ships.

Read

Crosby MC. The American Plague: The untold story of yellow fever, the epidemic that shaped our history. New York: Penguin; 2006.
Packard RM. The Making of a Tropical Disease: A short history of malaria. Baltimore: Johns Hopkins University Press; 2010.

Canal killer

When the French tried to build a canal through the Panama isthmus in the 1880s, they were forced to abandon their plans after they lost 22 000 workers to disease. The Americans later bought the rights to continue the project, along with the rotting French cranes and locomotives, but still faced the very real problem of endemic malaria and yellow fever. They turned to US Army surgeon William Crawford Gorgas (1854–1920) for help. Immune to yellow fever himself, thanks to contracting it in Texas, Gorgas had virtually eradicated the disease from Havana, Cuba, via an extreme mosquito-control programme. He did the same in Panama, ridding the Canal Zone of yellow fever within 16 months and enabling construction to begin.

William Crawford Gorgas, Sir Ronald Ross and Henry Claye Weeks on board the SS *Advance*
Photograph
E B Meyrowitz, 1904
L0011949 Wellcome Images

Gorgas (left) and the Secretary of the American Mosquito Extermination Society, Henry Claye Weeks (right), see off Sir Ronald Ross (centre), winner of the Nobel Prize for his discovery that malaria was transmitted by mosquitoes. He is bound for Panama.

The hut experiment

In 1900, three members of the newly founded London School of Tropical Medicine spent three months in a hut in a malaria-infested region near Ostia, Italy to test Dr Ronald Ross's (1857–1932) theory that malaria was transmitted by mosquito. By staying indoors from dusk until dawn they escaped infection. The team included Dr Louis Sambon (1865–1931), who was employed by Henry Wellcome three years later to tour Europe purchasing books and artefacts for Wellcome's collection.

Researchers outside the British experimental hut in Ostia
Coloured photograph of a drawing
Amedeo John Engel Terzi
41673i Wellcome Library

The net of privacy

Health organisations' recent efforts to encourage the uptake of long-lasting insecticide-treated mosquito nets in regions where malaria is endemic have been thwarted by privacy concerns. Research in Amazonian communities in Peru in 2007–8 showed that mosquito nets were used to divide living spaces into separate rooms and provide privacy. Traditional, less transparent, nets were therefore preferred. Study participants also reported using mosquito nets to conceal themselves from malicious spirits.

Advertisement for White & Wright's 'The Mosquito House'
From *Malarial Fever: Its cause, prevention and treatment*, 1902
Ronald Ross
b11505047 Wellcome Library

Souvenir species

Travellers have been picking up souvenirs, items kept as a reminder of their trip, for centuries. 'Souvenir species' act as a very different memento of where you have been; the term refers to parasites acquired from non-human hosts, such as those responsible for typhus or sleeping sickness. These uninvited visitors may be transmitted from other species through insect or animal bites, by preparing or eating contaminated flesh or via exposure to animal urine or faeces.

Giant killer bugs

The fictional threat of giant or mutated insects plays upon the human fear of swarms of poisonous or parasitical creatures bringing pain, death and disease. Mutant insects have featured in dozens of science-fiction books and (B-movie) films. A feared, alien 'other', they often function as a metaphor for contemporary anxieties about 'invaders' or frightening technology. In the 1995 film *Mosquito*, a spaceship crash-lands in a swamp, where the mosquitoes feed off alien corpses before mutating into giant man-killers.

A giant typhus louse threatens Russian soldiers
Colour lithograph
Russia, c.1921
545744i Wellcome Library

TRAVEL

Xenopsylla cheopis – oriental rat flea

Xenopsylla cheopis – oriental rat flea
Wax
Grace Edwards, 1914
RRa0275 / L0075809 Wellcome Images

Xenopsylla cheopis has mouthparts adapted to cutting the skin and sucking up blood. It is the primary vector for bubonic plague and typhus, transmitting bacteria as it secretes saliva to stop the host's blood coagulating.

⌀ The flea of death

Xenopsylla cheopis, or more precisely the bacteria *Yersinia pestis*, which it carries, is thought to be responsible for the Black Death, the epidemic of bubonic plague in the 1300s that originated in Asia before travelling across Europe. Believed at the time to travel through the miasma (see p. 91), the disease wiped out at least a quarter of the European population (over 25 million people). Plague outbreaks still occur, with one recorded in a Madagascan village in December 2013.

⌀ 'You all win or you all lose'

Unlike most board games, *Pandemic* requires players to cooperate with other competitors in a game dynamic the publishers pitch as 'you all win or you all lose'. Taking on the roles of researchers or members of the Centers for Disease Control, players must prevent outbreaks of viral diseases spreading around the world. Thanks to a random element and the way in which diseases spread, *Pandemic* can be a very difficult game to win.

First launched in 2008 (by Z-Man Games), a later version added the possibility for one player to act as a bioterrorist operating against the others; another edition allows players to develop a cure within a research lab.

Ornithodoros moubata

Ornithodoros moubata
Wax
Grace Edwards, 1914
RRa0276 / L0075811 Wellcome Images

The *Ornithodoros moubata* tick carries relapsing fever, a bacterial infection prevalent in Ethiopia and Sudan.

Glossina palpalis – tsetse fly larva

Glossina palpalis – tsetse fly larva
Wax
Grace Edwards, 1914
RRa0277 / L0075813 Wellcome Images

If it's able to source regular meals of blood, a female tsetse fly can produce a mature larva every ten days. While grabbing her life-giving meal, she may also transmit the (often fatal) sleeping sickness.

Diptera pupa

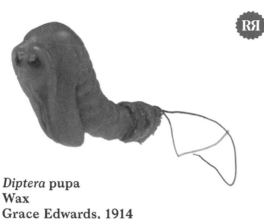

Diptera pupa
Wax
Grace Edwards, 1914
RRa0279 / L0075816 Wellcome Images

Phlebotomus papatasi – sandfly

Phlebotomus papatasi – sandfly
Wax
Grace Edwards, 1914
RRa0086 / L0075804 Wellcome Images

📄 Read

Crawford D. The Invisible Enemy: A natural history
   of viruses. Oxford: Oxford University Press; 2002.
Harrison M. Disease and the Modern World: 1500
   to the present day. Cambridge: Polity; 2004.
Honigsbaum, M. A History of the Great Influenza
   Pandemics: Death, panic and hysteria,
   1830–1920. London: IB Tauris; 2014.
Wolfe N. The Viral Storm: The dawn of a new
   pandemic age. London: Penguin; 2013.

📎 'Nothing spreads like fear'

Though Hollywood usually places more emphasis on drama than scientific accuracy, Steven Soderbergh's 2011 film *Contagion* has been praised as a realistic depiction of the outbreak of a new and rapidly spreading virus. Inspired by epidemics such as SARS and swine flu, *Contagion*, with the tagline 'nothing spreads like fear', documents the spread of a virus and the work of medical researchers and public-health officials to identify and contain it. The film explores the collapse in social order as the health panic takes grip, the impact of misinformation and disinformation on a terrified public and the competing interests at play throughout the pandemic.

🔍 The vector-maker

These over-sized models were commissioned in 1914 for the opening exhibition of the Wellcome Museum of Medical Science in London's Wigmore Street. Produced by Grace Edwards, an illustrator and model-maker employed unofficially by the Natural History Museum's entomology department, they were later displayed in the Natural History Museum's central hall. There, they helped Royal Army Medical Corps recruits familiarise themselves with disease-spreading invertebrates.

Grace Edwards with her models
Photograph
1926
C011/0141 Natural History Museum / Science Photo Library

Medicine chest

Medicine chest
Mahogany, brass and iron
1850–1900
RRa0105 / A30117 Science Museum /
L0076311 Wellcome Images

Whether used at home or abroad, a well-stocked medicine chest in the nineteenth century was likely to contain ingredients and preparations imported from overseas. In this example, two of the few remaining labels refer to tincture of rhubarb and essence of ginger, both plants introduced to Europe from Asia.

Genoese medicine chest
1562–66
A641515 Science Museum / L0058610 Wellcome Images

This sixteenth-century medicine chest still includes many of its original remedies, including rhubarb powder, ointment for worms, juniper water and mustard oil.

Well-travelled ginger

As far back as the fifth century, pot-grown ginger was being transported across the ocean, as protection against scurvy on board Chinese ships sailing to South-east Asia. The ancient Greeks and Romans used ginger for stomach and eye complaints and the plant is portrayed as an aphrodisiac in the *One Thousand and One Nights*.

In the Middle Ages, both live and dried ginger plants were being imported into Europe, and Henry VIII himself recommended ginger against the plague. Ginger soon made it across the Atlantic, where it was cultivated for export and shipped back to Europe in bulk. In a handy twist of fate, among ginger's many medicinal properties is the ability to prevent seasickness.

The great rhubarb hunt

Rhubarb has been known in China since the second millennium BCE and is still commonly used in Chinese medicine. Though Europeans had known about rhubarb since at least Marco Polo's times, and were able to procure it from a number of trading sources, the identity of the plant itself remained a mystery until the nineteenth century. This caused so much consternation that expeditions were dispatched to Russia, Tibet and India in search of the 'official' rhubarb plant. In 1790, an apothecary named Sievers travelled to Siberia on a rhubarb hunt for Catherine the Great. He failed in his quest.

My travels have satisfied me that as yet nobody – that is, no scientific person – has seen the true rhubarb plant. All the seeds procured under the name of true rhubarb are false; all the descriptions in all the Materia Medicas are incorrect.

Sievers reporting on his 1790 expedition

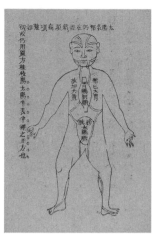

Describing the principles of diseases treated with cassia twig and rhubarb
Woodcut from *Shanghan Lun Dafang Tuje*, 1833
He Guifu
L0038030 Wellcome Images

Everest expedition Tabloid medicine chest
*c.*1933
A700004 Science Museum / L0059098 Wellcome Images

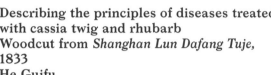

🖉 The first tabloids

The word tabloid might now be synonymous with sensational, celebrity-filled journalism, but the term was first coined by Henry Wellcome, who trademarked it in 1884. A combination of the components 'tablet' and '-oid', it was used to brand Burroughs Wellcome's new compressed-powder tablets, which delivered drugs in palatable doses. Wellcome later applied the term to a range of products, including the company's travelling medicine chests. By the early twentieth century, 'tabloid' was popularly applied to another compact and digestible item: the small-format newspaper.

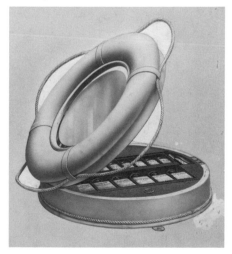

Tabloid medicine chest for yachts
*c.*1920
L0039097 Wellcome Images

Burroughs, Wellcome & Co.

"TABLOIDS"
Livingstone Rousers.

Jalap Pulv. 1½ *gr., Rhei Pulv.* 1½ *gr., Calomel* 1 *gr., Quinine Bisulph.* 1 *gr.*

The action of these is tonic, cathartic and antimalarial. One to three "Tabloids" may be taken with a little water, when an attack of malarial fever threatens, and repeat in two hours if necessary. These "Tabloids" are especially adapted for use as a general aperient in the tropics.

Snow Hill Buildings, LONDON.

Advertisement for "Tabloids"
Burroughs Wellcome and Co., 1896
L0074490 Wellcome Images

📖 Read

Harrison M. Contagion: How commerce has spread disease. New Haven: Yale University Press; 2013.
Laws B. Fifty Plants that Changed the Course of History. Newton Abbot: David & Charles; 2010.

Adjustable iron chair

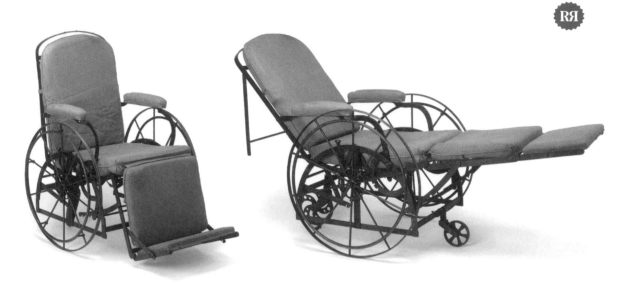

Adjustable iron chair
Metal, paint and upholstery
George Wilson, 1871
RRa0069 / L0075782 Wellcome Images

Patented in New York, George Wilson's adjustable chair could be shifted into several different positions, from armchair, to recliner to flat bed. It also folded into a compact form for transportation.

🖉 Transporting the sick and injured

Like the stretchers, litters and carrying chairs before them, wheelchairs were initially designed to transport sick and injured people from one place to another. The Roman Emperor Tiberius (42 BCE–37 CE) employed a corps of litter-bearers to carry wounded soldiers, and physicians in Rome prescribed transportation by litter, swing or hanging bed. All these methods required two bearers, and the patient usually remained in a prone position. It wasn't until the sixteenth and seventeenth centuries that wheels were added, allowing just one footman to propel someone in a barrow.

> *I dread a removal of the sick to Lisbon, the last cost us many men, and they must go on bullock carts: the next will cost us more in consequence of bad weather.*

Field Marshal the Duke of Wellington writing to Lieutenant General Sir John Sherbrooke, 1809

A man pushing a woman carrying a crutch
Etching with engraving
Follower of M Schongauer, 16th century?
43780i Wellcome Library

Mrs. FRENCH SHELDON'S PALANQUIN.

This palanquin was made at Whiteley's for Mrs. French Sheldon, the "Lady Stanley" who is bound for Central Africa, from designs by Mr. Henry S. Welcome (of Messrs. Burroughs & Wellcome, Snow Hill). It is a unique specimen of strong, light, and artistic cane and bamboo work, and Mr. Wellcome must be congratulated on his excellent taste. The palanquin will be carried by four of Mrs. Sheldon's Zanzibari porters.

Mrs French Sheldon's palanquin
Wood engraving
1891
L0023277 Wellcome Images

Produced for an explorer rather than a patient, this custom-made cane and bamboo covered litter was designed by Henry Wellcome for May French Sheldon's expedition to Africa.

✐ Wheel-chair maker

The invention of the bath chair at the end of the eighteenth century is attributed to John Dawson, who described himself as a 'wheel-chair' maker. Designed to carry patients to the therapeutic waters in Bath, the wheeled-chair could be steered by its occupant, but still required an attendant to push it.

'Warm trolleys' for transporting persons saved from drowning
Engraving from *Observations on Apparent Death from Drowning*, 1815
James Curry
b15052606 Wellcome Library

'A Medical Missionary Attending to a Sick African'

'A Medical Missionary Attending
to a Sick African'
Oil on canvas
Harold Copping, 1916

RRa0001 / 535948i Wellcome Library

Commissioned by the London Missionary Society
in 1916, this depiction of a western medical man at
work in Africa was used to publicise the organisation's activities. It shows a traditional local treatment
cast to one side in favour of a remedy taken from the
missionary's travelling medicine box, which bears
a striking resemblance to the Tabloid medicine chests
supplied to explorers by Burroughs Wellcome.

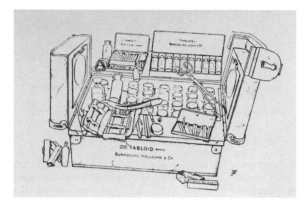

Tabloid medicine chest used
by Henry Morton Stanley
From *In Darkest Africa: Or the quest, rescue
and retreat of Emin, Governor of Equatoria,*
1890
Henry Morton Stanley
b13075998 Wellcome Library

'Prime joints of missionary'
Drawing
Burrage, 1860
572947i Wellcome Library

🖉 Healing body and soul

Though distinguished from pure evangelical
missionaries by their specialist training, medical
missionaries were still expected to know their Bible.
Until the 1920s, they engaged in evangelism as much
as medicine, effectively seeking to 'heal' both bodies
and souls. Their desire to transform beliefs was often
not realised, partly due to strong indigenous cultures
and partly because the visiting physicians lacked the
knowledge to be able to cure local diseases.

> *[Never neglect] the opportunity
> which the bed of sickness presents
> by saying a few kind words
> in a natural, respectful manner
> and imitate as far as you can the
> conduct of the Great Physician,
> whose followers we profess to be.*
>
> David Livingstone

Design for the *Uganda Jubilee Report
of the Mengo Medical Mission*
Pen and ink, with gouache
1927
22211i Wellcome Library

🖉 The first senders

The word mission (from the Latin *missionem*, meaning 'act of sending') originates from 1598, when the
Jesuits first sent monks abroad. In the 1890s, there
were 680 medically qualified Protestant missionaries
working worldwide. By 1916, this had risen to 1052
doctors and 537 nurses.

🗋 Read

Hardiman D. Healing Bodies, Saving Souls: Medical
    missions in Asia and Africa. Amsterdam: Editions
    Rodopi; 2006.

Midwifery set for developing countries

Midwifery set for developing countries
Covered aluminium case
and mixed materials
Seward Surgical, 1980
RRa0104 / 1981–1307 Science Museum /
L0076054 Wellcome Images

Obstetric equipment has traditionally been designed with portability in mind, since midwives generally travelled to attend mothers in their own homes. When working in remote locations, size and affordability become even more important.

⌕ Essentials only

In a drive to reduce size, weight and cost, this kit does not contain supplies that might be the norm in other regions – namely oxygen, resuscitation equipment, an intravenous drip, sutures, pain-relieving drugs or anaesthetics. It does include:

- 4 stainless steel bowls
- baby weigher
- measuring tape
- 4 pairs of scissors
- pair of tweezers
- 3 pieces of orange plastic tubing
- half-minute sand counter
- 100 disposable gloves
- plastic mat
- plastic aprons
- stainless steel mug
- 4 pairs of surgeons' gloves
- pack of umbilical cotton tape
- ear stethoscope
- nail brush
- coal tar soap
- orange plastic pumping tube
- plastic container

✎ Minimalist midwifery

A much more compact solution is the Kibiriti Kit developed by AMREF Health Africa in Kenya, which contains only soap, cloth and cotton wool swabs, wrapped string and a razor blade.

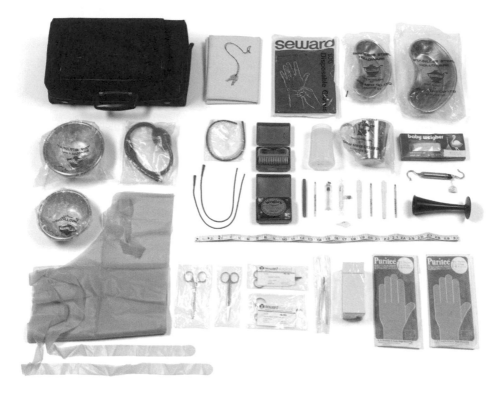

Contents of midwifery set
L0076055 Wellcome Images

The danger of motherhood

In 2007, UNICEF estimated that 99 per cent of the half a million women who die every year as a result of pregnancy complications or during childbirth live in developing countries, with one out of every 16 sub-Saharan African women likely to die in childbirth.

The home of midwifery

Midwifery was a recognised profession in ancient Egypt and, as the Old Testament reports, it was midwives who Herod ordered to carry out his murder of the innocents. The first recorded school of mid-wifery was set up in the Temple of Neith at Sais, and Egypt's modern School of Midwives was established in 1832, before those of many other countries. As chief instructor in the 1860s, female midwife Sitt Tamurhan even taught obstetrics to male medical students.

Midwife in Upper Egypt
Photograph
Winifred Swan Blackman, 1920s
26077i Wellcome Library

AIDS posters from around the world

When acquired immunodeficiency syndrome (AIDS) took the world by surprise in the 1980s, it sparked a swarm of health-education posters not seen since wartime warnings of the risks of foreign encounters. The rush of output by health providers, governments and design agencies is evidenced by the sheer number of posters relating to AIDS and HIV in the Wellcome Library (close to 3000, from 99 countries). Russia, China and most Middle Eastern countries are notably not represented.

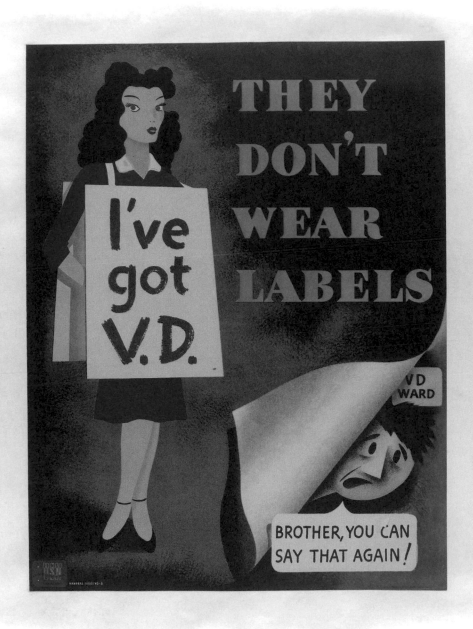

'I've got VD'
Colour lithograph
US Navy Bureau of Naval Personnel, 1948
580227i Wellcome Library

✐ The dangers of travel

Travel is a key theme for many of the posters, whether used literally or metaphorically.

A warning about foreign travel
NGO-AIDS Cell, Centre for Community
Medicine, All India Institute
of Medical Sciences
India, 1995
RRd0009 / 677435i Wellcome Library

'On holiday I forget everything
except a condom'
L'Agence Verte for SIDA Info Service
France, 1990s
RRd0025 / 672528i Wellcome Library

Kuwait Ministry of Health
Kuwait, 1995
RRd0028 / 677110i Wellcome Library

'Pleasure trips sometimes have too high
a price'
Papen WA for Federal Centre for Health
Education
Germany, 1990s
RRd0024 / 666150i Wellcome Library

🖋 Deathly warnings

While some posters attempt to communicate useful
information, others employ shock tactics.

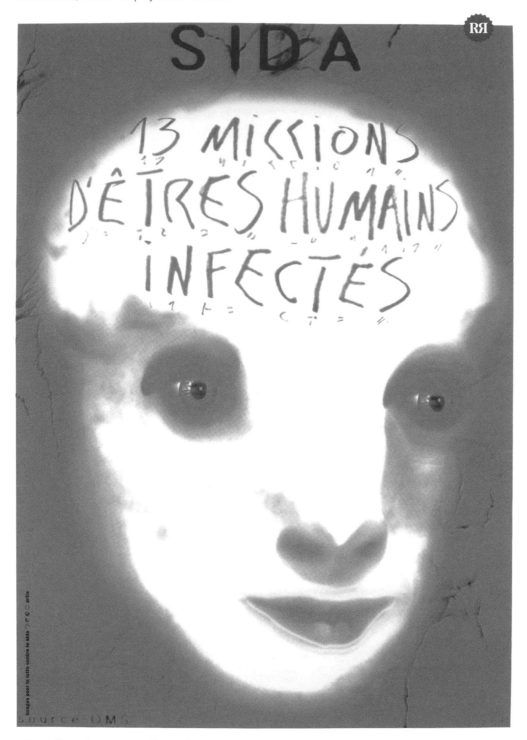

'13 million humans infected'
Zush for Artis
France, 1993
RRd0021 / 672783i Wellcome Library

Getting involved

Incorporating traditional imagery, these posters act as both warnings and calls to action, exhorting local communities to get involved.

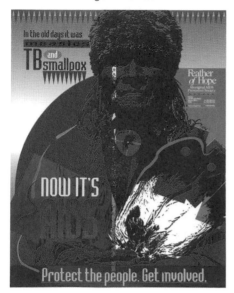

'Now it's AIDS'
**Sean Couchie for the Feather
of Hope Aboriginal AIDS Prevention
Society, Alberta
Canada, 1994**
RRd0041 / 668437i Wellcome Library

'Stop AIDS now'
**Charlotte Preden for Johannesburg City
AIDS Prevention Programme
South Africa, 1990s**
RRd0034 / 678937i Wellcome Library

Still ignorant

Since the first cases of what was initially named GRID (gay-related immunodeficiency) were spotted in San Francisco in 1981, 36 million people around the world have died as a result of contracting the human immunodeficiency virus (HIV). The poster epidemic may have subsided, but the public health challenge has not. Over 35 million people are thought to be living with HIV. Half of these may be undiagnosed, which brings new communication and management priorities.

'Ignore AIDS and it will bury
the rest of you'
**Pihas, Schmidt and Westerdahl
for the Oregon Health Division
USA, 1987**
RRd0012 / 668775i Wellcome Library

Read

Engel J. The Epidemic: A global history of AIDS. London: HarperCollins; 2006.
Fowler N. AIDS: Don't die of prejudice. London: Biteback Publishing; 2014.
World Health Organization. Public Health Campaigns: Getting the message across. Geneva: WHO; 2009.

TRAVEL

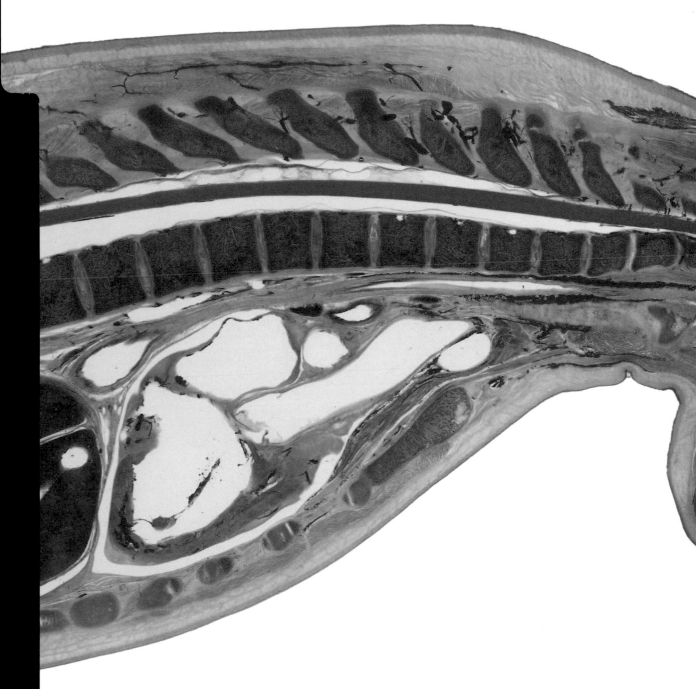

Lateral body slice
Gunther von Hagens, *c*.2000

Body

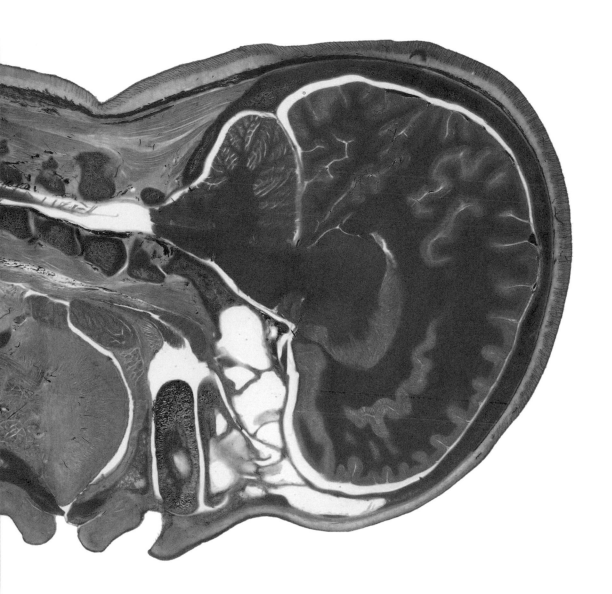

Visualisations of the body may be produced for learning and education, marketing and commerce, religious and spiritual purposes or as pure artistic expression. Taking time to explore, reflect on and reinterpret the body leads to new understanding about the nature of what it is to be human. Representations of the body also have the power to challenge accepted scientific knowledge, social norms and cultural beliefs.

The work of artists and anatomists has long been linked. While some Renaissance artists performed dissections in order to enhance their ability to accurately draw or sculpt the human figure, anatomists were publishing images of their own dissections, to be used as teaching aids. Some of the contemporary works in the Reading Room, like those by Luke Jerram and Helen Storey, have also been created in collaboration with scientific or medical specialists.

From colour printing and photography to microscopy, body scanning and digital rendering, new technologies create opportunities to obtain alternative views and perspectives on both the interior and exterior of the body. Applications of technology can also lead to new ways of interpreting, distributing or interacting with body imagery. In a more tangible sense, designers and engineers can also develop devices that may replace or extend parts of the body.

💬

The first object, then, in the Fine Arts is to represent man, and through his material form to represent man's feelings, passions, thoughts... Mr Gibbon [observes]... 'In these sublime arts the dexterity of the hand is of little avail, unless it is animated and guided by the most correct taste and observation'.

Robert Knox in *A Manual of Artistic Anatomy for the Use of Sculptors, Painters and Amateurs*, 1852

Lateral body slice

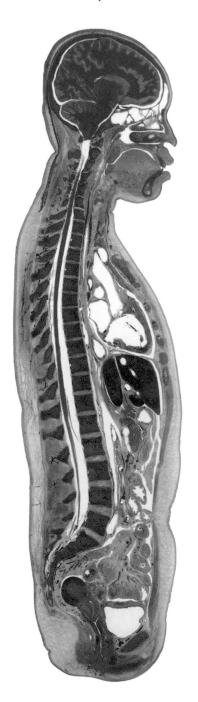

Lateral body slice
Human tissue and glass
Gunther von Hagens, *c.*2000
RRa0040 / L0075744 Wellcome Images

Despite describing his work as strictly medical, Dr Gunther von Hagens (b.1945) has more in common with Renaissance anatomists or entrepreneurial businessmen than many present-day scientists. It's therefore no surprise that his exhibitions of real plastinated cadavers have provoked outrage in – and challenges from – the anatomy establishment.

Von Hagens's *Body Worlds* shows transpose the traditional anatomical experience from the protected space of the academic dissecting room to public environments used for education or entertainment. Around the world, 38 million people have viewed the exhibitions; in Germany alone, 11 000 individuals have agreed to donate their corpses to the project.

✐ A selection of sections

In 1877, paint was injected into the arteries of a pregnant woman (who had died by hanging) before her body was frozen and cut into slices.

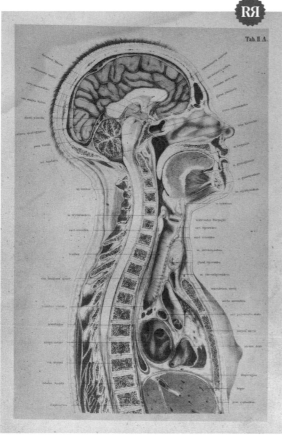

Plane section of a frozen woman
Woodcut from *An Atlas of Topographical Anatomy after Plane Sections of Frozen Bodies*, 1877
Wilhelm Braune
RRd0130 / b13228122 Wellcome Library

Vaccination pioneer Edward Jenner (1749–1823) was known for his delicate dissections. This flattened section of a stomach has been injected with wax to highlight the veins and arteries.

Stomach section
Edward Jenner, 1790–1823
A600030 Science Museum / L0057749 Wellcome Images

The Visible Human Project is a digital database of cross-sectional images of the human body made in 1994 for educational and research purposes. Produced by the US National Library of Medicine, it is based on sections of the frozen cadaver of Joseph Paul Jernigan of Waco, Texas, who was executed for murder.

✐ Sensational spectacle?

Von Hagens's plastinated bodies were well received on their first public outing at the National Science Center in Tokyo in 1995, but when the first *Body Worlds* exhibition in Germany was planned two years later, controversy abounded. The German Anatomical Society tried (unsuccessfully) to prevent the exhibition and later issued a statement saying the show severely violated the Society's principles. The document highlighted issues around the provenance of the plastinated bodies and scorned the use of 'the spectacular anatomy of the old days'. The Society, it seems, felt any public demonstration of contemporary scientific anatomy required 'sophisticated didactic methods'.

When *Body Worlds* came to London in 2002, the Anatomical Society of Great Britain and Ireland and the British Association of Clinical Anatomists also raised concerns about sensationalising and trivialising an important subject as 'mere spectacle'.

Read

Jones DG, Whitaker MI. Speaking for the Dead: The human body in biology and medicine. Farnham: Ashgate; 2009.

Lantos JD. Controversial Bodies: Thoughts on the display of plastinated corpses. Baltimore: Johns Hopkins University Press; 2011.

Quigley C. Dissection on Display: Cadavers, anatomists and public spectacle. North Carolina: McFarland; 2012.

The hat of nonconformity

Von Hagens is usually pictured sporting a distinctive black fedora similar to that worn by Dutch anatomist Nicolaes Tulp (1593–1674) in Rembrandt's 1632 painting 'The Anatomy Lesson of Dr Nicolaes Tulp'. According to von Hagens, Renaissance anatomists wore their hats at all times – even during dissections – as an expression of their independence from social norms.

**Model loosely based on
'The Anatomy Lesson of Dr Nicolaes Tulp'
Wood and ivory
18th century**
L0043756 Wellcome Images

**Reinier de Graaf discussing dissection
Engraving from *De Succi Pancreatici Natura et usu Exercitatio Anatomico Medica*, 1671
G Wingendorp**
25267i Wellcome Library

How to perform plastination

Although the word derives from the Greek '*plassein*' (meaning to shape or form), 'plastination' was developed by von Hagens in 1977, while working at Heidelberg University's Anatomical Institute. Von Hagens later patented his techniques and established a commercial company to sell plastination polymers and equipment. There are four key stages to his process:

1. Embalm the body and dissect it to display the internal structures.
2. Place in a bath of acetone, which diffuses into the body to replace the natural tissue fluids.
3. Vacuum-extract the acetone and gradually substitute it with liquid plastic.
4. 'Cure' the body with a special gas, which hardens the plastic.

The end result is a dry, odourless and durable 'specimen' that retains microscopic details and can be thinly sliced.

'Closing Neural Tube Dress'

RR

Spent four hours blasting information with Kate in the lab in Oxford. After three hours I couldn't take in any more: gastrulation, cell division, prophase, metaphase, telophase, neurulation, primitive streak, fibroblast, blastocyst and more. Spent the evening deciding on what level to pitch the understanding of the project. We decided that if our children can begin to understand the basic phases of our embryonic origins as a result of the collection, then we will have got it about right. The key recurring problem of the project raises its head: how to represent the science fact without the wearer looking a total prat.

Designer Helen Storey, April 1997

BODY

'Closing Neural Tube Dress'
Red fake fur
Helen and Kate Storey, 2014
(after the 1997 original)
RRa0070 / Helen and Kate Storey / Wellcome Images

Designer Helen Storey and her sister Kate, an embryologist, collaborated to create this dress illustrating an early stage of embryonic development.

In a healthy human, the transformation (or 'neurulation') of a flat sheet of tissue into the 'neural tube' stretching the length of the embryo usually occurs between 18 and 28 days after conception. The brain and spinal cord then develop from this hollow structure.

Neurulation in a chick embryo
Light micrograph
Kate Storey
B0008179 Wellcome Images

This image of a bird embryo captures the same stage of development illustrated in Helen and Kate Storey's dress. After 28 hours, the blocks of tissue that will go on to form the bird's vertebrae are clearly visible alongside the central neural tube.

'A Man Holding an Écorché Statuette'

RЯ

BODY

'A Man Holding an Écorché Statuette'
Oil on canvas
Italian, late 18th–early 19th century
RRa0090 / 44581i Wellcome Library

Although the term 'écorché' was not introduced until the nineteenth century, models revealing human muscle structure were used in art teaching from the 1700s. The flayed statuette held by this artist is based on a much-reproduced model by Italian painter and architect Ludovico Cigoli, known as il Cardi (1559–1613).

RIGHT: Écorché with raised left arm
Red-chalk drawing
After Ludovico Cigoli, 17th century
38055i Wellcome Library

🗎 Read

Petherbridge D, Jordanova L. The Quick and the Dead: Artists and anatomy. Berkeley: University of California Press; 1997.

Wallace M, Kemp M. Spectacular Bodies: The art and science of the human body from Leonardo to now. London: Hayward Gallery; 2001.

Drawing from death

Artists such as Leonardo da Vinci (1452–1519) and Michelangelo Buonarrotti (1475–1564) improved their knowledge of anatomy by performing their own dissections. Early in his career, Michelangelo was given access to a dissecting room and – thanks to the permission granted by a papal brief – a supply of corpses by the prior of the Augustine monastery Santo Spirito in Florence. The artist's contemporary biographer Ascanio Condivi reports, however, that Michelangelo gave up the practice when he could no longer stomach handling cadavers.

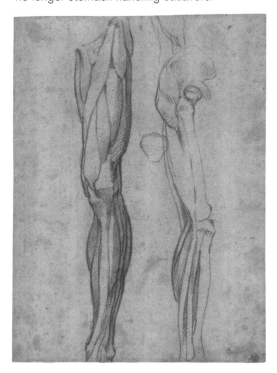

The muscles of the legs
Drawing
Michelangelo Buonarrotti, 1515–20
26058i Wellcome Library

Resurrection men

Ever since early dissections in the third century BCE, sourcing corpses has been a troublesome and often gruesome business. Surgeons and anatomy students in the eighteenth century procured cadavers from prisons, hospitals and freshly dug graves. As demand grew, and surgeons sought to distance themselves from such unsavoury behaviour, an organised and lucrative trade in grave-robbing developed. Warring gangs of 'resurrectionists' or 'sack-'em-up men' were so prevalent in London that armed vigilantes policed burial grounds.

An 'honest trade'

In Charles Dickens's *A Tale of Two Cities*, young Gerry Cruncher is keen to observe his father at the work he describes as the 'honest trade' of 'fishing'. The boy secretly follows Cruncher senior as he leaves home in the early hours one day, carrying a sack, crowbar, rope and 'other fishing tackle'. When Gerry sees his father pry open a coffin pulled from the depths of the local graveyard, he dashes home. Unsurprisingly, there is no fish for breakfast the next day.

Though the practical details of Dickens's story may be inaccurate, his depiction of the rascal Cruncher was in keeping with public perceptions of real-life resurrection men.

'The Resurrectionists',
Messrs Cruncher and son
Frederick Barnard, c.1876
b11103115 Wellcome Library

♀

The body-snatchers
they have come,
And made a snatch at me;
It's very hard them kind of men
Won't let a body be.

You thought that
I was buried deep,
Quite decent like and chary,
But from her grave in Mary-bone
They've come and boned
your Mary.

From the pathetic ballad 'Mary's Ghost'
in Gibson's *Rambles in Europe in 1839*

Anatomical wax moulages

Eczema of the hand

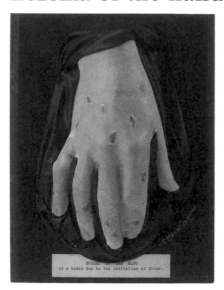

Eczema of the hand
Wax
C Mauer-Jagow, *c.*1930
RRa0072.1 / L0075793 Wellcome Images

Variola vera discreta (discrete smallpox)

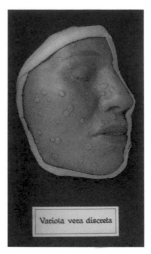

Variola vera discreta (discrete smallpox)
Wax
***c.*1930**
RRa0072.3 / L0075795 Wellcome Images

Acne of the hand

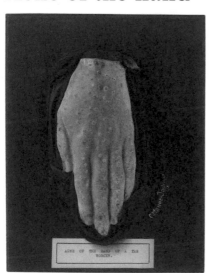

Acne of the hand
Wax
C Mauer-Jagow, *c.*1930
RRa0072.2 / L0075794 Wellcome Images

Ritter's disease

Ritter's disease
Wax
***c.*1930**
RRa0072.4 / L0076292 Wellcome Images

'St Anthony's Fire'

RR

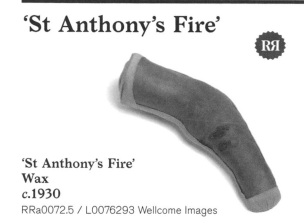

'St Anthony's Fire'
Wax
c.1930
RRa0072.5 / L0076293 Wellcome Images

The art of wax moulage (from the French for moulding or casting) is particularly well-suited to creating realistic representations of afflictions of the skin. Casts such as these, showing the pathology of dermatological or venereal diseases, were common medical teaching tools in the nineteenth century. Produced by skilled artisans, they focused attention on localised symptoms and allowed prolonged and more careful study than would dissecting-room samples.

A secretive craft

Moulage artists took plaster casts directly from diseased patients, filled them with waxes and resins, employed coloured wax for scabs and glass bubbles as blisters. They even inserted real hairs to bring the finished models to life. Their craft was a secretive business and many took details of their techniques to their graves.

For 'Instruction and Delight'

Although these twentieth-century casts hail from the Wellcome Museum of Medical Science, the public exhibition of anatomical waxworks in London dates back a further 200 years. In 1719, anyone with a shilling to spare could view one of Italian-trained surgeon Guillaume Desnoues's models at a grocer's shop in the Strand. Advertisements pitched the display as 'Instruction and Delight' for those 'unskill'd in Anatomy'.

Desnoues's models were later incorporated into the less-than-salubrious collection of Rackstrow's Museum, which also contained 'diseased wombs', 'children still-born, preserved in spirit', 'miscarriages or abortions' and 'monstrous births' from women and beasts. One of Rackstrow's most famous exhibits was a wax model of a heavily pregnant woman, complete with 'blood' (represented by red liquid) passing through its glass veins.

Artistic differences

Two pioneers of anatomical moulage fell out over what might be described as artistic differences. Sicilian abbot Giulo Gaetano Zumbo (1656–1701) had a penchant for illustrating the realities of bodily decomposition, as seen in his allegorical wax tableaux of plague and syphilis. When Zumbo partnered with surgeon Guillaume Desnoues (1650–1735) to make moulages of Desnoues's dissections in Genoa, it wasn't exactly a meeting of minds. Desnoues aimed to produce models that could be viewed without the horror of the corpse. He disliked the tomb-like quality of Zumbo's approach so much that they went their separate ways.

Zumbo's models were later praised by the French Académie Royale des Sciences and his reputation was secured when he presented the wax models depicted below to Louis XIV; the king responded by granting Zumbo an exclusive licence to practise his craft. Many of Desnoues's models, on the other hand, served out their last days in a seedy museum on London's Fleet Street.

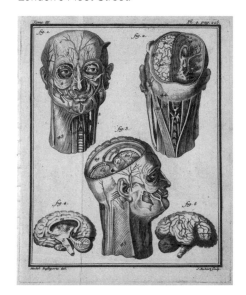

**Wax models of the head and neck
made by Giulo Gaetano Zumbo
Engraving
Jean Robert after Madeleine Basseporte,
1749**
34190i Wellcome Library

Read

Anderson J et al. The Art of Medicine: Over 2000 years of medicine in our lives. Lewes: ILEX; 2011.
Schnalke T. Diseases in Wax: The history of the medical moulage. Michigan: Quintessence; 1995.

BODY

A dissected man with separate sections of the brain

RR

**A dissected man with separate
sections of the brain
Oil on canvas
Jacques Fabien Gautier Dagoty, 1764–65**
RRa0003.1 / 44573i Wellcome Library

Almost 150 years after it was painted, this vividly
coloured panel was described by the *Lancet* as
'a remarkable adornment to any great medical library
or institute'. Yet the French virtuoso Jacques Fabien
Gautier Dagoty (1710–85) is better known as
a pioneer of three- and four-colour printing than
as a painter.

Dagoty improved on the mezzotint process
initially developed by his tutor Christophe Le Blon
(1667–1741) and also obtained the exclusive royal
licence to use it. In so doing, he brought life and tone
to the world of anatomical reproductions and created
opportunities to sell images of the body in multiple
formats. While a printed version of the brain dissections shown here had earlier appeared in his 1748
book *Anatomie de la Tête en Tableaux Imprimés*,
the entire composition was also produced and sold
as a lurid life-sized print.

The anatomist's printer

When Padua-based Andreas Vesalius (1514–64)
published his influential anatomy book *De Humani
Corporis Fabrica* (*On the Fabric of the Human Body*)
in 1543, he sent his manuscript all the way to Basel
to be printed, requesting particular care be taken
with the illustrations. 'These have not been executed
merely as simple outlines like ordinary diagrams in
textbooks,' he wrote, 'but have been given a proper
pictorial quality.'

**From *De Humani Corporis Fabrica*, 1543
Andreas Vesalius**
b11536196 Wellcome Library

'The Flayed Angel'

Dagoty's best-known anatomical print is sometimes
called 'The Flayed Angel'. Originally published in the
1745 anatomical album *Essai d'Anatomie en Tableaux
Imprimés*, which Dagoty co-produced with physician
and anatomist Joseph Guichard Duverney (1648–
1730), the image found more recent fame when
displayed in Gunther von Hagens's *Body Worlds*
exhibition (see p.61).

**Colour mezzotint illustration from *Essai
d'Anatomie en Tableaux Imprimés*, 1745–46
Jacques Fabien Gautier Dagoty**
572024i Wellcome Library

⊘ A master of gloss and spin

Dagoty varnished his colour prints to conceal the imperfections caused by multi-plate printing, and to impart the glossy texture of an oil painting. He also embellished his own image and reputation, adding 'Dagoty' to his given name of Gautier and publishing personal treatises on colour theory (which challenged the established views of Descartes and Newton) in his own illustrated scientific journal.

Two dissected men with a separate section of viscera

Two dissected men with a separate section of viscera
Oil on canvas
Jacques Fabien Gautier Dagoty, 1764–65
RRa0003.2 / 44572i Wellcome Library

Colour printing can nowhere make a greater contribution to scientific understanding than in anatomy.

Dagoty's publishing partner,
Joseph Guichard Duverney

⊘ Following in Estienne's footsteps

The father of French anatomy is generally considered to be Charles Estienne (*c.*1504–64), who published the works of Galen and Sylvius and also produced his own three-volume anatomy publication *De Dissectione Partium Corporis Humani Libri Tres.*

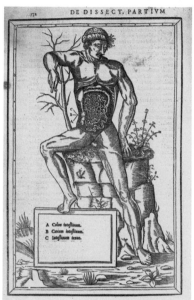

Male figure with intestines exposed
Woodcut from De Dissectione Partium Corporis Humani Libri Tres, 1545
Probably by Stephanus Rivierius
b11536901 Wellcome Library

▢ Read

Kusukawa S. Picturing the Book of Nature: Image, text and argument in sixteenth-century human anatomy and medical botany. Chicago: Chicago University Press; 2012.

Laurenza D. Art and Anatomy in Renaissance Italy: Images from a scientific revolution. New York: Metropolitan Museum of Art; 2012.

Richardson R. The Making of Mr Gray's Anatomy: Bodies, books, fortune, fame. Oxford: Oxford University Press; 2008.

BODY

Pregnant woman from the shack of a voudun practitioner

BODY

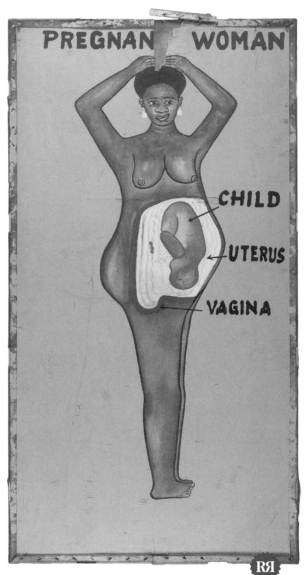

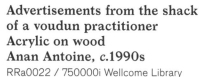

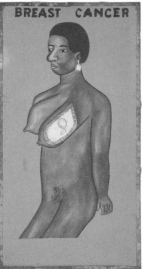

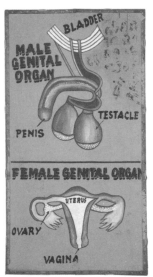

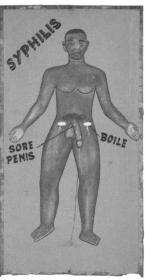

**Advertisements from the shack
of a voudun practitioner
Acrylic on wood
Anan Antoine, c.1990s**

RRa0022 / 750000i Wellcome Library

Until August 2010, these advertisements for voudun health services stood alongside stalls selling vegetables, clothes and electronic gadgets in a busy African marketplace. Salvaged from the outer walls of a shack in the Benin town of Adjarra, all six graphic panels dwell less on the results of the proffered cures and more on the afflictions themselves.

The trade of advertising is now so near to perfection, that it is not easy to propose any improvement. But as every art ought to be exercised in due subordination to the public good, I cannot but propose it as a moral question to these masters of the public ear, Whether they do not sometimes play too wantonly with our passions...

'Art of Advertising' in the *Idler*, 1759

✐ Healthy customers

Images of the body are familiar sights on promotional material for health services and pharmaceutical remedies. In these examples, the advertisements present fantastical or aspirational illustrations of the alleged benefits to users.

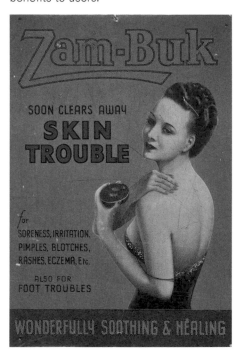

Zam-Buk showcard
c.1930
L0030507 Wellcome Images

Hazeline Snow advertising
1930s
L0033937 Wellcome Images

Ayer's Cathartic Pills advertising
b15600385 Wellcome Library

'Glass Microbiology'

'Giardia'

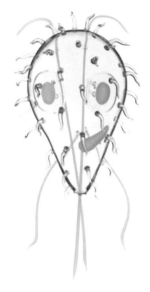

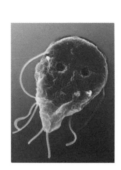

LEFT: **'Giardia'**
Glass
Luke Jerram, 2014
RRa0270 / L0076096 Wellcome Images

RIGHT: **Giardia**
Scanning electron micrograph
David Gregory and Debbie Marshall, 2003
B0004813 Wellcome Images

'MRSA'

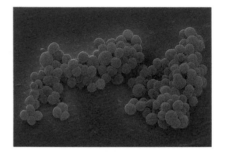

TOP: **'MRSA'**
Glass
Luke Jerram, 2014
RRa0272 / L0076098 Wellcome Images

BOTTOM: **MRSA**
Scanning electron micrograph
Annie Cavanagh, 2008
B0006889 Wellcome Images

'Ebola'

'Ebola'
Glass
Luke Jerram, 2014
RRa0271 / L0076097 Wellcome Images

'Adenovirus'

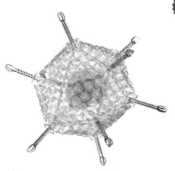

'Adenovirus'
Glass
Luke Jerram, 2014
RRa0273 / L0076143 Wellcome Images

Colour-blind multidisciplinary artist Luke Jerram's (b.1974) transparent sculptures challenge how bacteria and viruses are often visualised. Designed in consultation with virologists from the University of Bristol, Jerram's artworks, which have featured in the *Lancet* and the *British Medical Journal* and on the cover of *Nature*, exhibit an intrigue and accuracy often missing from photographic representations.

> *In this...new and amazing world there is displayed a beauty, a perfection, adaptation and reproduction, surprisingly surpassing those objects with which we are familiar in every-day life. With the microscope we search into the mysteries of creation, and detect many of the secret workings of nature.*

J Hogg in *The Microscope: Its history, construction and teachings*, 1854

Seeing in colour

Carl Zeiss Jena Microscope
Wellcome Images

The development of staining techniques was as crucial to the scientific success of the microscope as improvements in the depth and quality of magnification. Dyes have been used to identify different microscopic tissues for over a hundred years, with multiple stains employed to pinpoint a range of individual structures.

Some of the most commonly used stains (and the substances they are used to mark) are:
- carmine – for glycogen,
- coomassie blue – for proteins,
- crystal violet – for cell walls,
- malachite green – for spores and
- safranin yellow – for collagen.

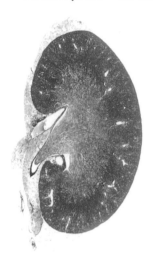

Stained kidney cross-section
Wellcome Images

Black-and-white photographic images captured by electron microscopes are often artificially coloured for both scientific purposes and emotional effect. Whatever the purpose, the addition of colour strongly influences how the image is understood and interpreted.

> *The problem is that you end up with a percentage of the public believing that viruses are these brightly coloured objects. These are often portrayed in newspapers as having an air of scientific authenticity and objective truth, whereas actually that isn't the case. Viruses are so small they have no colour. They're smaller than the wavelength of light.*

Artist Luke Jerram

BODY

The microbial enemy

Anios disinfectant image
G de Trey-Maison, 1910
460155i Wellcome Library

Virulently coloured images accompanied by doomsday headlines or grisly storylines reinforce long-standing views of microbes as aggressive invaders. In this French advertisement for Anios disinfectant, microbes are shown as grotesque bug-eyed beasts.

Science-fiction film *The Andromeda Strain* followed a band of scientists developing an antidote to a deadly microbe that came from outer space. The desperate scientists are shown staring at large projections of (colourful) crystalline patterns of the growing microbe; each protagonist seems to hold a different view about what these striking images represent.

Read

Breidbach O et al. Art Forms in Nature: Prints of Ernst Haeckel. London: Prestel; 1998.

Broll B. Microcosmos: Discovering the world through microscopic images. Ontario: Firefly Books; 2010.

Jackson L. From Atoms to Patterns: Crystal structure designs from the 1951 Festival of Britain. Somerset: Richard Dennis; 2014.

Insulin fabric

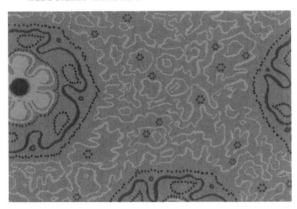

Insulin fabric
2014
AOC / Wellcome Images

The fabric used to upholster the soft furnishings in the Reading Room depicts a simplified reproduction of biochemist Dorothy Hodgkin's (1910–94) drawing of insulin. Originally sketched in the 1930s, Hodgkin's image provided inspiration for the Festival Pattern Group, 28 manufacturers who developed textiles and other homewares for the 1951 Festival of Britain based on X-ray diffraction photographs of crystals. The new fabric is based on the screen-printed wallpaper used in the Thames-side Regatta Restaurant during the festival.

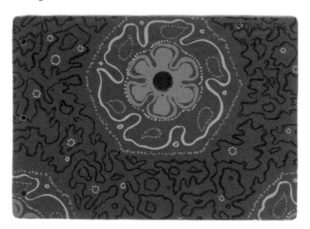

Insulin 8.27 hand screen-printed wallpaper
W J Odell, *c.*1951
Victoria and Albert Museum, London

The body in stereo

tween your eyes. When observed as a stereo pair, they should therefore deliver a three-dimensional view. If you don't have a stereoscope, you can hold a piece of card between the two images, so that each is only seen by a single eye.

> *[The Edinburgh Stereoscopic Atlas of Anatomy] affords a ready means of refreshing the memory in a graphic and realistic way upon many anatomical points of practical importance which most medical men find it difficult to retain.*
>
> 'Notices of Books', *Journal of Anatomy and Physiology*, April 1905

Stereoscope and the *Edinburgh Stereoscopic Atlas of Anatomy* edited by David Waterston, 1905
RRc0001.1–.2 / L0075862 Wellcome Images

Dating back to the 1830s, the stereoscope – derived from the Greek words *stereos* (solid) and *skopein* (to see) – was originally a form of parlour entertainment. By the early twentieth century, its potential as a teaching aid for medical students had been spotted and the *Edinburgh Stereoscopic Atlas of Anatomy* published. The atlas comprised high-quality photographs of carefully dissected specimens.

Stereo photos

Though stereoscopy predates photography, the two technologies have an interdependent relationship: photography led to a stereoscope boom in the 1850s, while the stereoscope added extra depth to the objective truth associated with photographic images.

How to snap a stereoscopic image in three steps

1. Stand with your feet side by side.
2. Put the weight of your body on one leg and take a picture.
3. Transfer your weight on to the other leg and take another shot.

The resulting views will be captured from positions roughly the same distance apart as the space be-

'No home without a stereoscope'

'No home without a stereoscope': so went the slogan of the London Stereoscopic Company in 1856, who also claimed, 'for a wedding present a stereoscope is unsurpassed'. The company offered mass entertainment packaged as slides of antiquities, foreign locations, 'drawing-room elegancies' and 'toothaches and woes'.

> *The time will come when a man who wishes to see any object, natural or artificial, will go to the Imperial, National, or City Stereographic library and call for its skin or form, as he would for a book at any common library.*
>
> 'The Stereoscope and Stereograph' in *Atlantic Monthly*, June 1859

Read

Barry SR. Fixing My Gaze: A scientist's journey into three dimensions. New York: Basic Books; 2010.

Pohl Omniskop X-ray machine

📎 The mysterious X-rays

On 8 November 1895, German physicist Wilhelm Röntgen (1845–1923) discovered X-rays while investigating whether cathode rays could pass through glass. It took another 17 years before fellow physicist Max von Laue discovered that the mysterious X-rays were short-wavelength electromagnetic waves. Röntgen received the first ever Nobel Prize for Physics, in 1901.

💬

We are sick of the Röntgen rays...
you can see other people's bones
with the naked eye, and also
see through eight inches of solid
wood. On the revolting indecency
of this there is no need to dwell...
Perhaps the best thing would
be for all civilized nations to
combine: to burn all works on the
Röntgen rays, to execute all the
discoverers...

Pall Mall Gazette, 20 March 1896

Pohl Omniskop X-ray machine
Wood, steel and rubber
Germany, 1925–35
RRa0023 / A600315/1 Science Museum /
L0076296 Wellcome Images

One of the earliest X-ray machines that could be rotated around a patient, the Omniskop was used by Berlin-based doctor Ernst Rachwalsky for almost four decades. Launched a few years before the wide understanding that over-exposure to X-ray radiation could be harmful, the machine enabled doctors to capture a number of images from different angles, helping to improve diagnoses. The reactions of patients who 'rode' in the machine ranged from 'frightened' to 'fascinated'.

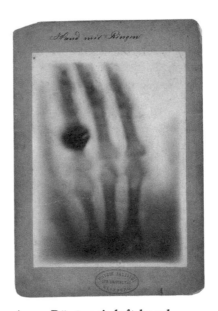

Anna Röntgen's left hand
Photoprint from a radiograph
by Wilhelm Röntgen, 1895
32971i Wellcome Library

🔍 Hybrid name

The brand name '*Omniskop*' is probably derived from the Latin for 'all' (*omnis*) and the Greek for 'to see' (*skopein*).

I have seen my death!

Anna Röntgen on seeing the bones
within her hand

BODY

'A fairy tale'

Writing in 1896, German physicist Otto Lummer reported:

> 'In reading the preliminary communication, 'On a New Kind of Rays,' sent to me by Professor Röntgen a few days ago, I could not help thinking that I was reading a fairy tale, though the name of the author and his sound proofs soon relieved me of any such delusion. There it was printed in black and white, that one could photograph metal weights in a closed wooden box, and that one could print the bones of the living hand upon the photographic plate as if by magic.'

A premonition of death

In Thomas Mann's novel *The Magic Mountain* (1924), protagonist Hans Castorp sees his cousin Joachim undergo an X-ray, and is alarmed by the sight of a beating heart. When he asks for his own hand to be X-rayed, he sees that 'which no man was ever intended to see and which he himself had never presumed he would be able to see: he saw his own grave.'

All-seeing eyes

The ongoing appeal and intrigue of seeing beneath the skin is encapsulated in 'X-ray specs', a product commonly advertised in the back pages of comic books. The 'amazing' glasses illustrate the broader human desire to know more and – as with comic-book heroes and the foes they face – to acquire superhuman abilities.

Read

Glasser O. Wilhelm Conrad Röntgen and the Early History of the Roentgen Rays. San Francisco: Norman Publishing; 1989.

Gunderman RB. X-Ray Vision: The evolution of medical imaging and its human significance. New York: Oxford University Press; 2013.

Mould RF. A Century of X-rays and Radioactivity in Medicine: With emphasis on photographic records of the early years. London: Institute of Physics Publishing; 1993.

Looking inside mummified bodies

Although dissections of mummified bodies date back to at least the 1650s, the first modern medical autopsy was conducted by Augustus Bozzi Granville (1783–1872) in 1825. Granville noted the dimensions of bones and body parts, estimated the age at death and made a stab at the cause of death. The Reading Room's virtual autopsy table allows visitors to explore inside a number of mummified bodies in a less intrusive way, thanks to the power of medical imaging and digital rendering.

'Mummy unrollings'

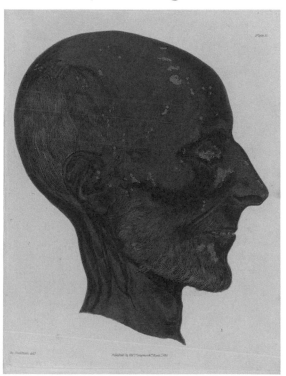

Plate from *A History of Egyptian Mummies and an Account of the Worship and Embalming of Sacred Animals by the Egyptians*, **1834**
Thomas Joseph Pettigrew
b12830653 Wellcome Library

In 1833, Thomas Joseph Pettigrew (1791–1865), the son of a surgeon-turned-apothecary, embarked on a campaign of public 'mummy unrolling' that would help transform mummified bodies from anatomical specimens to manufactured entertainment experiences. Pettigrew's unrollings took place in hospitals and scientific institutions, but were attended by princes, peers and members of parliament. In one sold-out event at the Royal College of Surgeons, those unable to gain entry to the crowded room included the Archbishop of Canterbury and the Bishop of London.

Chambers's Edinburgh Journal reported spectators on a similar occasion feeling 'delight in witnessing the unrolling of endless bandages, smiling at the hieroglyphics, and then staring at the dried remains of a being who moved on the earth three or four thousand years ago'. Mummy unrolling wasn't just a *visual* spectacle, though; audiences could touch and smell fragments of the cloth wrappings or the bodies themselves, and investigators such as Granville even tasted samples as part of their analyses.

> *Some nasty beasts met together on Saturday last to indulge in the disgusting amusement of 'unrolling a mummy'. Our old friend Pettigrew, commonly called Mummy Pettigrew, was the principal unroller on this filthy occasion. Pettigrew seems positively to do nothing else but unroll mummies... [he] glories in the unclean process, and pulls about the encrusted carcase with a fervour of purpose which may be scientific, but which is nonetheless nasty in the extreme.*

'Scientific Mummery', *Figaro in London*, 1837

As a savvy marketer, when Pettigrew sought to publish a substantial work on the history of Egyptian embalming he included printed prospectuses for his publication along with the unrolling invitations that he dispatched to Egyptologists, antiquarians, scientists and lords. *A History of Egyptian Mummies and an Account of the Worship and Embalming of Sacred Animals by the Egyptians*, an accessibly written text illustrated by George Cruikshank (who would later apply his talents to Charles Dickens's works) is still considered a valuable and admirable contribution to the field.

Read

Sugg R. Mummies, Cannibals and Vampires: The history of corpse medicine from the Renaissance to the Victorians. Abingdon: Routledge; 2011.
Luckhurst R. The Mummy's Curse: The true history of a dark fantasy. Oxford: Oxford University Press; 2012.
Roach M. Stiff: The curious lives of human cadavers. London: Penguin; 2003.

Virtual autopsy technology

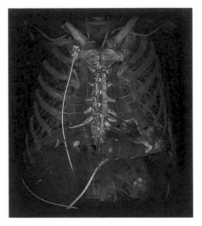

Mechanical heart pump in the thorax
Computed tomography
Anders Persson, 2013
B0009361 Wellcome Images

This image, produced by Swedish radiologist and researcher Anders Persson, won the 2014 Wellcome Images Awards. It uses the same imaging technology that allows virtual autopsies to be performed.

Persson's method is to capture 'sliced' images of the patient as X-rays and combine these to create a three-dimensional digital model, which can be rotated, sectioned and zoomed into. Separate tissue layers, such as bone, fat and even air can be digitally manipulated to turn them transparent, opaque or coloured, allowing medical personnel to view the parts of the body that are most pertinent to their investigation.

Medicinal mummy

The remains of mummified Egyptian bodies were sought after for their medicinal properties from at least the tenth century, and *mummia* or *mumia* is thought to have been administered to Henry VIII as a remedy. Traders keen to satisfy demand raided ancient tombs and mummified the newly dead in order to generate enough stock.

> *From these sarcophagi, mummia, which is the oil of those dead persons, is extracted and this the physicians give to sick patients with fractures.*

12th-century Andalusian geographer Al-Zohri describing the ancient burials of Alexandria

Egyptian baby

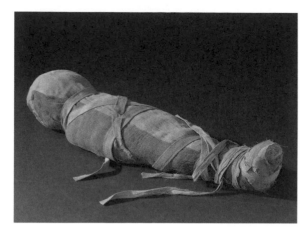

**Mummified male infant
(age at death: 0–2 months)
Egypt, 1069–664 BCE**
A634914 Science Museum / L0058419 Wellcome Images

In October 2013, three mummified bodies acquired for Henry Wellcome in the 1920s were imaged using Siemens high-resolution CT scanners at London's Brompton Hospital. The data was reviewed by an expert team of curators and technologists from the British Museum, UCL, the Interactive Institute and IMA Solutions. As well as generating data that will be of interest to historians and anthropologists, the study of mummified cadavers may provide information about how present-day diseases have evolved.

Chimu burial

**Mummified male youth
(age at death: 17–25 years)
Southern Peru, 1000–1470 CE**
A31655 Science Museum / L0035650 Wellcome Images

One of a pair of mummified bodies bought at auction in 1924, this body was sold as part of a collection called 'Native Curios'. The auction catalogue recounted a detailed back story for this young man, who was supposedly 'trussed up and buried alive for eloping with the daughter of the chief of a neighbouring tribe'. Of course, the tale may well have been fabricated in an effort to enhance the sale price.

Rope basket burial

**Mummified male child
(age at death: c.11 years)
Southern Peru, 1400–1800 CE**
A301301 Science Museum

The curse of the mummy

In April 1923, two days after amateur Egyptologist Lord Carnarvon died, the *Express* newspaper ran the front-page headline 'Egyptian collectors in a panic'. The report claimed people all over Britain were sending their Egyptian treasures to the British Museum for fear of the wrath of 'ka', the double of Tutankhamen's soul who was popularly blamed for Carnarvon's death. Museum records refute the *Express*'s claims about receiving an 'avalanche' of 'shrivelled hands and feet', yet the fear of the mummy's curse still lives on, at least in journalists' minds. In 2014, the London *Metro* spiced up a bland story about a relatively unknown film director leaving Universal Pictures's latest mummy movie with the headline 'The curse of The Mummy strikes again'.

'Free'

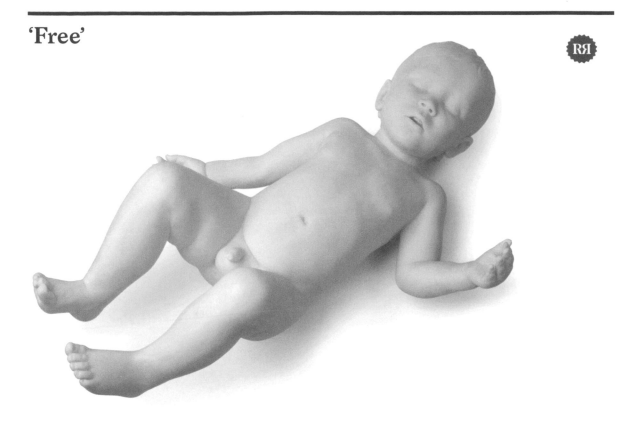

BODY

'Free'
Polymer wax
Marc Quinn, 2005
RRa0064 / L0075764 Wellcome Images

'Free' is a sculpture of British artist Marc Quinn's (b.1964) son Lucas. The title alludes to both the material used to create the work and the health of Quinn's son, who previously suffered from a life-threatening allergy to milk. A year before, Quinn made a similar sculpture from polymer wax mixed with the synthetic milk substitute that kept Lucas alive. When his son recovered, Quinn made 'Free' uncontaminated with additional ingredients.

Quinn intended these sculptures to appear as if floating just above the floor, to enhance the concept of his son's vulnerability.

📖 Read

Cronin E. Mermaid: A memoir of resilience. New York: Norton; 2014.

Medus-Mansell L. No Hand to Hold and No Legs to Dance On. Treharris: Accent Press; 2009.

Ott K et al. Artificial Parts, Practical Lives: Modern histories of prosthetics. New York: New York University Press; 2002.

Gas-powered prosthesis

Gas-powered prosthesis
Plastic, metal and textile
Steeper, 1963
RRa0315 / 1999-578 Science Museum /
L0076322 Wellcome Images

Prostheses are often thought of as cosmetic or functional replacements for parts of the body that have been lost. These CO_2-powered arms, custom-made for a child born with malformed limbs due to Thalidomide, extend rather than replace the natural body. Valves connected to a leather waist-belt by a nylon cord brought the spade-like hands together when the child leant backward, or opened them as they leant forward. Heavy and cumbersome, the device covered the user's own arms (where the shoulder, elbow and hand or fingers might be absent), inadvertently preventing the young child from using them and depriving them of sensation.

...a person who has never had a limb just doesn't seem to understand what an arm or leg is like. And although I've seen quite a few patients who have been born without...particularly without arms, they're desperately keen to have arms because they want to look the same as other people... we know they'll never wear them. But you've got to find out for yourself and it doesn't feel normal to them.

Dr Ian Fletcher, who designed and fitted this prosthesis while working at Queen Mary's Hospital, Roehampton, interviewed in 2011 for *Thalidomide: An oral history*

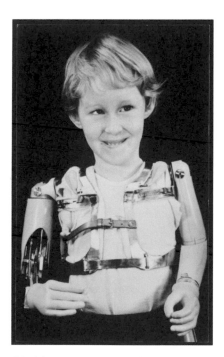

Child in prostheses from Queen Mary's Hospital, Roehampton
Photograph
1977

Yvonne Kavanagh / Thalidomide Society

[The prosthetics] were uncomfortable, sometimes painful and always disabling. As a child I was led to believe the prosthetics were for my benefit in order to make me more capable as every other child, even though I was more independent without them.

Edward Freeman, interviewed in 2011 for *Thalidomide: An oral history*

The 'long arm'

In 1786, American author, scientist and diplomat Benjamin Franklin (1706–90) invented a machine for 'taking down Books from High Shelves'. Incorporating a grasping 'thumb' and 'finger', and controlled by a length of cord Franklin called a 'sinew', the 'Long Arm' was made from an eight-foot-long piece of pine.

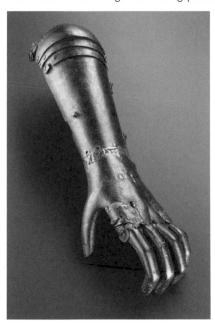

Articulated prosthetic arm
Germany, 1560–1600
A121449 Science Museum / L0057510 Wellcome Images

Functional toes

Prosthetic toes have been found on or with some ancient Egyptian mummies. Originally thought to have been a cosmetic addition, intended to complete the body after death, researchers have now shown that these toes could be effective aids when walking while wearing sandals.

Woman in later life

Woman in later life
Plaster
Jane Jackson, 1930s
RRa0081 / L0075796 Wellcome Images

Woman with Cushing's syndrome

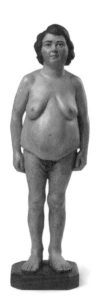

Woman with Cushing's syndrome
Plaster
Jane Jackson, 1930s
RRa0082 / L0075798 Wellcome Images

Boy with rickets

Boy with rickets
Polyester resin
Jane Jackson, 1930s
RRa0083 / L0075802 wellcome Images

Conditions such as Cushing's syndrome and rickets, along with the familiar changes associated with old age, transform the shape of the human body from its youthful and healthy 'norm'. In each case, the obvious physical changes are accompanied by less-visible symptoms – from emotional disturbances and depression to pain in the limbs, hypertension and osteoporosis.

✐ The ideal human form

Notions of the ideal human date back to ancient times. Plato (*c.* 428–*c.* 348 BCE) considered sight to be the noblest of the five senses, and beauty is usually characterised by visual appearance. The relatively constant shape of the human form prompted Classical scholars to invent mathematical rules governing its proportions.

In the fifth century BCE, the Greek sculptor of athletes Polykleitos set out his prescription for human beauty in a text called the *Canon*, and used these proportions to create an exemplary bronze nude of a young man carrying a spear, the *Doryphoros*. Unfortunately, neither the text nor the sculpture survive.

The system of human proportion laid down by the Roman architect Vitruvius (*c.*80–*c.*15 BCE) has fared better. In his scheme, the height of a man was four cubits (the length from elbow to fingertips) or six feet. Other major features of the human form could be described in similar basic ratios. Working 1500 years later, Leonardo da Vinci converted these ideal dimensions into the well-known diagram of a human figure enclosed by a circle and a square, known as 'Vitruvian Man'.

Vitruvian Man
Woodcut from *M. Vitrvvivs per Iocvndvm Solito*
Castigatior Factvs cvm Figvris et Tabvla
vt iam Legi et Intelligi Possit, 1511
Vitruvius Pollo
b1153815 Wellcome Library

Detail of 'Liquid Ground 1'
Helen Pynor, 2011

Breath

Invisible and essential, breath is symbolic of what it means to be human and alive. First and last breaths mark the start and end of life, and we can, on occasion, rouse the seemingly dead by resuscitating them. But breath is about more than functional respiration. Almost a sense in itself, breath is taken away by astonishing events, held in anticipation, caught and saved. Sights and sounds may be inhaled like air, while exhaled sighs express unspoken feelings.

Unlike other bodily functions – such as digestion or circulation – the unconscious management of breath may be overruled. Taking control of the body's movements and breathing deeply can help manage stress and anxiety and increase lung capacity. In Buddhist meditation, the aim of focused breathing is to achieve a higher state of consciousness, in which breath is reconnected with the spirit.

Aristotle considered breath a nutrient, to be digested like food. While oxygen may indeed be required to feed muscles and organs, the lungs may also be exposed to therapeutic vapours and perfumes, atmospheric pollution and tobacco smoke. The role such environmental factors play in bronchial health can create stark social strata of chronic disease.

> *Observe yourself and you will find that your thoughts and breaths are not only correspondent, but instantaneously coincident: if you think deeply you breathe deeply; if you hold thought you hold breath.*
>
> James Wilkinson in *Epidemic Man and his Visitations*, 1893

'Liquid Ground 1'

'Liquid Ground 1'
Photographic print
Helen Pynor, 2011
RRa0109 / Helen Pynor

Helen Pynor's 'Liquid Ground' series explores connections between the human body and water. In this print, the physically displaced organs appear strangely at home floating in their watery surroundings, which mirror the body's own internal fluids.

Pynor (b.1964) began the series while living and working beside the Thames at Woolwich, the site of a mass drowning that was the worst peace-time disaster to occur within Britain.

'550 lives lost'

On a warm late-summer evening in 1878, the pleasure cruiser SS *Princess Alice* steamed towards London Bridge ferrying over 700 day trippers back from Gravesend and Sheerness. At Gallions Reach, just outside Woolwich, the *Princess Alice* was hit by a steam collier ship four times her size and sliced in half. She sank in under five minutes.

Many passengers were trapped within the wreck and drowned within sight of the boat's exits. Others were plunged into the most polluted water in the Thames, where millions of gallons of raw sewage had been released just an hour before. Over 500 people died, the majority of them women.

Nearly all rushed to the aft part of the steamer. As the bow subsided gradually under water the shrieks were fearful, and nothing could be done to save life... the river for a hundred yards was full of drowning people screaming in anguish and praying for help.

The *Illustrated Police News*, 7 September 1878

Feminine tears

In literature, drowning is often associated with the feminine, emphasising the liquid characteristics of the female body: water (in feminine tears), menstrual blood and amniotic fluid. This may explain why drowning is regularly meted out as a symbolic death for female characters, as was the fate of Ophelia in Shakespeare's *Hamlet*.

Hero Henry

In 1885, the Royal Humane Society awarded Henry Wellcome a medal for 'having saved life from drowning'. Wellcome had been canoeing on the Thames with American author Annie Wakeman when the pair were swamped by water in Boulter's Lock.

I at once made a dive after her and after a desperate struggle against the terrible currents brought her to the surface only to be sucked down again, but finally I saved her after the most desperate struggle I have ever experienced. Miss W showed the greatest pluck for she never struggled but allowed me to hold her without the slightest hindrance...

Henry Wellcome describing his canoeing incident, 1885

Henry Wellcome's Royal Humane Society medal for saving life 'from drowning'
L0076149 Wellcome Images

Death by drowning

The World Congress on Drowning defines drowning as 'the process of experiencing respiratory impairment from submersion/immersion in liquid'. Anyone submerged in water automatically holds their breath. As carbon dioxide levels rise, they involuntarily inhale, gasping for air but taking in liquid. Within minutes, they fall unconscious due to lack of oxygen in the brain. Even if water is removed from the lungs, death occurs when the oxygen deficiency becomes irreversible, a fate influenced by the age of the victim and the temperature of the water. Those who have survived drowning describe the experience as lethargic, dull and painless.

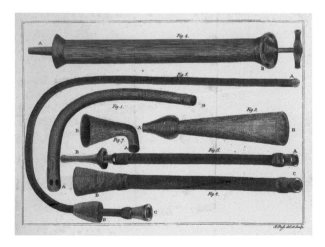

Instruments for those drowned
From *Popular Observations on Apparent Death from Drowning, Suffocation etc.*, 1812
J Curry
L0016573 Wellcome Images

**Two techniques for dealing
with someone rescued from drowning
Taki Rankei, 1790**
L0031459 Wellcome Images

· ·

🗋 Read

Hoare P. The Sea Inside. London: Fourth Estate;
2013.

· ·

📎 The professional mermaid

**Mermaid
Coloured engraving from *Encyclopaedia
Londinensis*, 1795–1815
J Pass**
3331i Wellcome Library

Linden Wolbert is a free diver who can reach
a depth of 35 metres while holding her breath.
Wolbert wears a prosthetic silicone mermaid tail
and describes swimming with it as the most transcen-
dental feeling she's ever experienced. Describing
herself as a 'professional mermaid', Wolbert appears
at children's parties and corporate events.

'Breath'

**'Breath'
Charcoal and acrylic on card
David Marron, 2013**
RRa0282 / L0076190 Wellcome Images

Depicting a newborn between breaths and cries,
'Breath' represents the circular process of respiration
and, ultimately, life. The body's internal gaseous
exchanges are shown wrapping over and around the
baby, uniting the unseen breath with the creation
of new life.

Artist and paramedic David Marron (b.1972) has
witnessed many problematic births. He's delivered
babies in the backs of cars and on the pavement, and
seen newborns struggling to take their first breaths.
The birth of his own son was long and traumatic.
Despite being present at many other births, hearing
the sound of his own child's first cry was a new
experience for Marron.

🖋 First gasps

Weeping baby
From *The Anatomy and Philosophy*
of Expression as Connected
***with the Fine Arts*, 1844**
Charles Bell
L0031754 Wellcome Images

A baby usually takes its first breath, which sounds more like a gasp, within ten seconds of emergence. As the child inhales, the tiny air sacs (alveoli) of the lungs inflate for the first time, causing the baby to cry. It may also cough and splutter as it expels amniotic fluid from the lungs.

🖋 The 'sneeze of life'

In Maori culture, speeches always start with the phrase '*Tihei mauri ora*', meaning 'the sneeze of life'. The words recall the first breath of a newborn child and celebrate the essence of life. '*Tihei mauri ora*' is a sign that the airways are ready to be used, that the speaker claims the right to speech and that they are also someone to whom it's worth listening.

🖋 Laughing to death

The intercostal muscles responsible for breathing are also used to talk and laugh. In a competition between breathing, talking and laughing, laughter will win out, as a fan of the 1970s TV show *The Goodies* discovered: Alex Mitchell reportedly laughed himself to death while watching the 'Ecky-Thump' episode.

'This Fatal Subject'

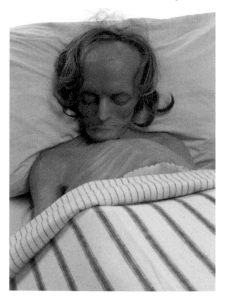

'This Fatal Subject'
Silicone, animatronic mechanism
and mixed materials
Eleanor Crook, 2008–09
RRa0066 / L0075772 Wellcome Images

In deliberate contrast to the dense, deceased flesh that sculptor and anatomical artist Eleanor Crook (b.1966) encounters in medical dissecting rooms, 'This Fatal Subject' touches on what Crook describes as 'the lightness of evanescent breath'. This dynamic sculpture portrays the threshold moment when the body transitions from a person to a defunct body as an almost invisible, inaudible and unannounced event.

💬

Stilling the quiver of the skin
as the dying sets in; the settling
of the accordion ribcage, a few
tilts of the head at the final
thoughts; thoughts of something
inconsequential perhaps,
or a reverie; perhaps a fear the
subject is too weak to express,
or just a wonder that the desire
for one more breath is at last over.

Sculptor Eleanor Crook on 'This Fatal Subject'

🖋 The death-rattle kiss

The death rattle is a distinctive and unsettling signal that the end of life is near. As muscles in the tongue and palate weaken, patients are unable to clear their airways, and the body's natural secretions gather in the throat and upper chest, rattling with every breath. The idea is used to terrifying effect by *Harry Potter* author J K Rowling (b.1965) in her depiction of the 'dementors', the ghoulish guards of the wizard prison Azkaban. These metaphors for depression suck the air 'with the sound of a death-rattle'. Because the dementors feed on others' warmth and happiness, their victims feel as if they are 'drowning in cold'. For those unfortunate souls caught escaping from Azkaban, punishment comes in the form of 'the dementor's kiss', the sucking out of their soul – like a breath – from their mouth.

🖉 Life in an iron lung

To the poliomyelitis patients it was designed to help, the coffin-like iron lung was a fearful symbol of almost certain death. Many placed in the sealed box died within it, and some never regained the ability to breathe unaided. For those who escaped after the worst stage of the disease had passed, a lasting fear of death by asphyxiation was a common side effect.

Working on the principle of negative pressure, air is sucked out of the iron lung, expanding the patient's chest and causing them to involuntarily inhale. When the pressure increases, the diaphragm contracts and air is forced out of the body. The portholes on the side of the sealed box provide access for medical staff, but also allow the internal pressure to drop. This might leave patients gasping desperately for breath as they are nursed.

While most patients who survived in the iron lung would regain the ability to breathe within weeks or months, some relied on their artificial respirator for years or even decades.

Iron lung *c*.1950
A683097 Science Museum / L0059081 Wellcome Images

📄 Read

Williams G. Paralysed with Fear: The story of polio. Basingstoke: Palgrave Macmillan; 2013.

Cresolene Vaporizer

Cresolene Vaporizer
Carton, paper, glass, metal and cloth
Vapo-Cresolene Co., 1880–93
RRa0038 / A640110 Science Museum /
L0076014 Wellcome Images

Designed for night-time use, this ornate vaporiser generated strong-smelling fumes, to be inhaled as the patient slept. The paraffin lamp heated a dish filled with Cresolene, a coal-tar derivative presented by its manufacturer as 'the safest and simplest method of destroying infection'. In the days before advertising standards, Vapo-Cresolene was claimed to be an effective treatment for whooping cough, croup, colds, asthma and diphtheria. It was also pitched as a remedy for distemper, pneumonia, coughs and colds in horses and dogs.

The most popular inhalation device in late nineteenth-century America, the Vaporizer's instructions caution that 'Cresolene imparts a burning sensation to the skin and is poisonous if taken internally'.

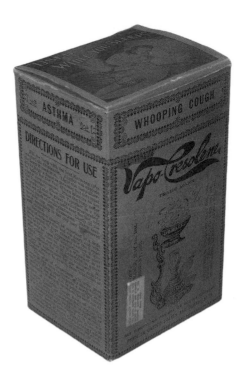

Vapo-Cresolene Co. packaging
A640110 Science Museum / L0058539 Wellcome Images

A woman inhaling vapour
From *Arzneibuch: Compendium of popular medicine and surgery, c.1675*
L0042101 Wellcome Images

🔍 An extraordinary cure?

In 1908, chemists from the American Medical Association laboratory analysed Cresolene and concluded it was 'a member of that class of properties in which an ordinary product is endowed with extraordinary virtues'. Today, inhalation treatments are no longer considered effective for whooping cough; the antiseptic fumes have no effect on the bacteria that cause the complaint, and inhaling them only irritates the cough.

✎ Snorting and sniffing

The practice of inhaling vapours dates back several thousand years: ancient Egyptians snorted fumes from burning pine resins and bitumen; Hindu surgeon Susrata (*c.*500 BCE) circulated incense or sulphur fumes in the operating theatre; and Hippocrates (*c.*460–*c.*370 BCE) employed fumigated sulphur as a treatment.

Hippocrates is also credited with ridding Athens of the plague by burning garlands of flowers and sweet-scented unguents to generate clean air. When the Black Death hit Europe in the fourteenth century, the belief that the plague was transmitted through poisonous fumes (known as 'miasma') prompted people to carry herb or flower nosegays to sweeten the air.

Protective clothing for plague
Watercolour
1910
2084i Wellcome Library

Silver-plated bronchitis kettle

Silver-plated bronchitis kettle
Silver plate, ivory and glass
R & J Slack, 19th century
RRa0112 / A625885 Science Museum /
L0076058 Wellcome Images

Bronchitis is an infection of the larger airways of the lungs, which causes irritation and inflammation. In the nineteenth century, bronchitis kettles were commonly used to moisten the air and aid breathing. Those who couldn't afford a high-end device such as this, fashioned their own by attaching rolled cones of brown paper to everyday kettles.

The patient is attacked
with a sense of constriction,
or other uneasy feeling at the
chest: his breathing is hurried,
anxious, laborious; the efforts
of all the voluntary muscles
which can be called into action,
rendering the oppressed state
of the lungs sufficiently evident.

Charles Badham in *An Essay on Bronchitis:*
With a supplement containing remarks on
simple pulmonary abscess, Etc, 1814

The English disease

Chronic bronchitis was first described in 1808 by London physician Charles Badham. The condition became known as the 'English disease', due to high mortality rates compared with other countries. In the 1960s, bronchitis was the third most common cause of death in England, occurring in over a third of men over 30 and responsible for almost 30 000 deaths in a single year. The death rate varied across the country, with the highest rates in heavily populated industrial cities.

Bronchitis is now most commonly seen as chronic obstructive pulmonary disease, which has an estimated prevalence of 3.7 million in the UK (of which around 1 million cases are thought to be undiagnosed). Air pollution has been overtaken by smoking as the most common cause of the condition.

The Peril in the Air, **published by Peps Company to promote its cough and cold tablets 1913**
b16766477 Wellcome Library

The world's worst jobs

In 1832, Leeds physician Charles Turner Thackrah published *The Effects of Arts, Trades, and Professions on Health and Longevity*, a book linking diseases with specific working conditions. Thackrah listed chronic bronchitis as a frequent malady of men working in dusty employments, such as cloth dressers and croppers, Cornish miners, coffee roasters, leather dressers, flaxmen and metal button-makers.

Sir Hiram Maxim's 'Pipe of Peace'

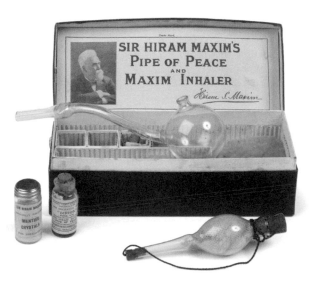

Sir Hiram Maxim's 'Pipe of Peace'
Glass, rubber, cloth and netting
Hiram Maxim, *c.*1910
RRa0113 / 1981-982/2 Science Museum /
L0076316 Wellcome Images

American inventor Sir Hiram Stevens Maxim (1840–1916) devised this inhaler to treat his own chronic bronchitis. The swan-necked pipe allowed vapours from Maxim's calming remedy to be delivered to the back of the throat. With characteristic humility, Maxim called his concoction 'dirigo', the Latin for 'I lead'. The mixture combined menthol with pine, wintergreen and sweet birch essences.

A killing machine

Despite his impact on the hundreds of thousands of people who bought his pipe in the early 1900s, Maxim has a rather different lasting legacy – as inventor of the automatic machine gun. He also developed an automatic mousetrap, the first sprinkler system activated by fire and a carbon-based electric light (in use before Thomas Edison's better-known incandescent bulb). While Maxim's early steam-powered airplane only left the ground briefly, his Captive Flying Machines fairground rides were installed outside the Crystal Palace and at Blackpool Pleasure Beach. The application of his skills to the Pipe of Peace was a step too far for Maxim's friends, though, one of whom accused him of 'prostituting his talents on quack nostrums'.

From the foregoing it will be seen that it is a very creditable thing to invent a killing machine, and nothing less than a disgrace to invent an apparatus to prevent human suffering.

Sir Hiram Maxim

Hiram Maxim (centre)
and Henry Wellcome (right)
at the feast of the Thanksgiving Day
Banquet of the American Society of London
From an original drawing by
Herbert Johnson, 1896
L0033982 Wellcome Images

Read

Connor S. The Matter of Air: Science and the art of the ethereal. London: Reaktion Books; 2010.

BREATH

Inhaling chloroform

Sir James Y Simpson and friends insensible after experimenting with chloroform
Pen and ink
1840s
545210i Wellcome Library

After its discovery in 1831, the organic solvent chloroform was initially drunk in solution as a treatment for asthma and persistent coughs. The popular version of how it came to be used as an anaesthetic recounts Edinburgh professor James Young Simpson inhaling it with friends after a dinner party. Simpson's maid is said to have come into the room to find all the diners asleep.

Within two years, Charles Dickens's wife Catherine had inhaled chloroform as an anaesthetic during labour. When Queen Victoria did the same, the approach became known as 'chloroform à la reine' (*like the queen…*).

Chloroform cocktails

Former *Cosmopolitan* editor Helen Gurley Brown's bestselling guide to 1960s life, *Sex and the Single Girl*, includes a recipe for 'Chloroform cocktails'. Brown advises mixing extremely strong coffee (six cups boiled down to one), a bottle of gin and a litre of vanilla ice cream.

Parachute proof

'ESO' chloroform apparatus
Longworth Scientific Instrument Co., 1945
A630964 Science Museum / L0058301 Wellcome Images

The portable Epsten Suffolk Oxford (ESO) machine, built to withstand a parachute drop, was used to anaesthetise battle casualties during World War II. Cheap, non-flammable and relatively fast-acting, chloroform had overtaken ether (see p. 121) as the military anaesthetic of choice during the Crimean War, a century before.

‘Robbery by means of chloroform’

In 1850, the *Pharmaceutical Journal* reported the trial of two women of 'notorious character', who chloroformed a man walking down Whitechapel Road in London's East End. The victim claimed to have woken up naked in a wretched apartment, without his watch, money and some of his clothes. Two weeks after the attack, he was still suffering from physical after-effects.

Although tales of robbers, highwaymen and kidnappers using chloroform-soaked rags to wicked ends abound in nineteenth-century literature and the popular press, in reality the substance did not have the instantaneous effects these stories relied on. Chloroform was also difficult to administer safely and, in inexpert hands, might lead to convulsions and death.

Read

Stratmann L. Chloroform: The quest for oblivion. Stroud: The History Press; 2013.

Tobacco pipe

Tobacco pipe
Meerschaum, brass, horn and hose
19th century
RRa0034 / A653265 Science Museum / L0076013 Wellcome Images

Unlike cigarettes that dwindle away as the tobacco burns, pipes are permanent symbols. They also prolong the smoking process: a pipe must be prepared and packed before it is lit and the tobacco periodically tamped down during smoking. Smoking a pipe is a contemplative and ceremonial act and, as any reader of Sherlock Holmes knows, a pipe – and the way it is smoked – says a lot about its owner. This elaborate example is thought to be made in the image of Napoleon I's wife, Joséphine, Empress of France from 1804 to 1809.

> *Pipes are occasionally of extraordinary interest. Nothing has more individuality save, perhaps, watches and bootlaces.*
>
> Sherlock Holmes in Arthur Conan Doyle's
> *The Adventure of the Yellow Face*, 1893

A purifying healer

When European explorers brought tobacco back from the Americas in the fifteenth century, they transformed smoking from a magical ritual to a hedonistic pastime. Tobacco played a pivotal role in North and South American healing and religion, where shamans smoked to achieve trance states and blew purifying and reinvigorating smoke fumes over patients to ward off evil spirits.

Your face is on fire!

The practice of smoking was so unfamiliar to sixteenth-century Europeans that Sir Walter Raleigh was supposedly doused by one of his servants, who thought his face was on fire.

Sir Walter Raleigh being doused with water as he smokes
Wood engraving
Mid 19th century
25007i Wellcome Library

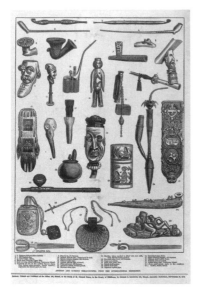

Tobacco pipes from around the world
Wood engraving from *The Illustrated
London News, c.1873*
After J T Balcomb
25000i Wellcome Library

'Smokey Sue Smokes for Two' doll

RЯ

'Smokey Sue Smokes for Two' doll
Plastic, rubber and wool
Adam Rouilly Ltd., 1995
RRa0035 / L0076131 Wellcome Images

With a wholesome look reminiscent of 'Orphan Annie', Smokey Sue uses shock tactics to discourage young people from smoking. The pregnant doll's demonstration of nicotine and tar passing into the jar of 'amniotic fluid' (actually water, which turns brown as Sue 'smokes') may not be scientifically accurate, but the message is clear.

Itty Bitty Smoker

Another anti-smoking doll, Itty Bitty Smoker, positions a cigarette directly in the mouth of a tiny model foetus. Part of 'The Womb of Doom', Itty Bitty is designed to show 'who really winds up puffing on the 4000-plus toxins in tobacco smoke'.

Don't shock, tax!

In a 1999 study, economists Peter Bardsley and Nills Olekalns found anti-smoking advertising and education had no effect on smoking behaviour. Analysing 35 years of policy interventions, the pair identified taxation of tobacco products as the most effective way of reducing overall tobacco consumption. Other research suggests fear-based anti-smoking initiatives have no impact on young people whose self-esteem is linked with smoking. Shocking ads may also provoke defensive responses in committed smokers.

Read

Gilman SL, Zhou Z. Smoke: A global history of smoking. London: Reaktion Books; 2004.
Hilton M. Smoking in British Popular Culture 1800–2000: Perfect pleasures. Manchester: Manchester University Press; 2000.

Unfit for cannibals or God

Anti-smoking views were expressed in Europe almost as soon as tobacco arrived from the Americas. James I and VI published (initially anonymously) a pamphlet about the 'manifolde abuses of this vile custome' in 1604.

Two centuries later, Victorian anti-tobacco campaigner Thomas Reynolds invoked powerful fantastical stories in his crusade against 'the devil's weed'. Reynolds claimed smokers were left undevoured by cannibals due to their unsavoury tobacco-taste, that Napoleon and Guy Fawkes made their misguided decisions while under the influence of tobacco and that tobacco defeated the designs of God.

> *A custome lothsome to the eye, hatefull to the Nose, harmefull to the braine, dangerous to the Lungs, and in the blacke stinking fume thereof, nearest resembling the horrible Stigian smoke of the pit that is bottomelesse.*

King James I and VI in *A Counter-Blaste to Tobacco*, 1604

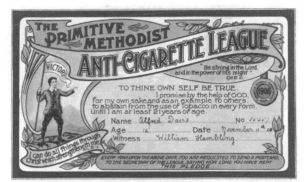

A pledge to abstain from smoking until the age of 21
Primitive Methodist
Anti-Cigarette League, 1906
b16557050 Wellcome Library

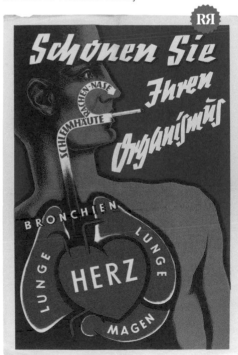

Poster showing smoke circulating through the heart and lungs
Colour lithograph
Germany, c.1900
RRd0144 / 642527i Wellcome Library

World War I horse gas mask

World War I horse gas mask
Leather, jute, iron, canvas, fibre and resin
Germany?, 1914–18
RRa0036 / A635089 Science Museum / L0058466
Wellcome Images

Gas masks were a regular feature of life in World War I – for horses, dogs and men. Between 1916 and 1918, 200 British horses died from gas poisoning and a further 2000 were treated for skin and eye irritations.

Designed to prevent damage to the sensory organs – a horse's nose and mouth or a man's nose, mouth and eyes – the protective masks actually placed soldiers and animals in an enforced state of sensory deprivation. Soldiers were instructed to fit horse masks before their own, because horses couldn't be taught to hold their breath.

The chemist's war

Known as 'the chemist's war', World War I became a scientific cat-and-mouse game as nations desperate to end the stalemate of trench warfare developed ever more effective chemical weapons. At the Battle of Ypres in 1915, German forces introduced chlorine, a gas that severely irritated the nose, mouth and lungs and caused death by drowning. The French followed, with phosgene, which the Germans then combined with chlorine to make a mixture colloquially known as 'white star'. In 1917, the Germans first used mustard gas, which caused more casualties than all the previous chemical weapons combined.

World War I gas mask
Germany, 1915–18
A637236 Science Museum / L0058505 Wellcome Images

𝒪 Death by sneezing

Heavier than air or water, corrosive mustard gas flowed into trenches and ditches and could penetrate rubber and leather. On initial exposure, it produced few physiological symptoms; the first British soldiers to encounter it simply started sneezing. Within a couple of hours, though, burns and blisters develop and unprotected eyes may be blinded. In extreme cases, the lungs practically disintegrate.

📖 Read

Croddy E. Chemical and Biological Warfare: A comprehensive survey for the concerned citizen. New York: Springer-Verlag; 2002.
Rex C. Doodlebugs, Gas Masks and Gum: Children's voices from the Second World War. Stroud: Amberley Publishing; 2012.

𝒪 Arsenic and old hemp

The trenches of the Great War weren't the first battlefields to fall under clouds of deadly gas. Motivated by similar desires to break up bedded-in sieges, the Greeks and Chinese deployed smoke and gas in the fourth and fifth centuries BCE. Greek historian Thucydides (460–395 BCE) refers to Spartan armies using toxic clouds of arsenic vapour, while Chinese sappers lowered burning bundles of hemp into the tunnels of enemy mines.

𝒪 A multi-purpose tool

Concerned by the threat of poison gas being released on home soil, in the run-up to World War II the British government manufactured enough gas masks for the entire population. Forced to carry their masks everywhere, children soon found multiple uses for them: as disguises when they were up to no good; to protect their eyes when slicing onions; or even to filter out noxious fumes left behind in the lavatory.

Death by poisonous gas released into the air
Coloured lithograph
Women's International League
for Peace and Freedom, 1920s
RRd0156 / 640521i Wellcome Library

BREATH

Stethoscope

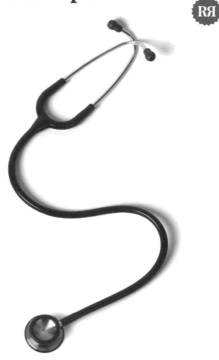

Stethoscope
Littman, 2014
RRc0008 / Wellcome Images

When French physician René Laënnec (1781–1826) consulted an overweight female patient in 1816, he considered it improper to place his head directly on her body to listen to her chest. Instead, Laënnec rolled a sheet of paper into a tube, placed one end on the patient and the other to his ear, thereby inventing a diagnostic tool that is as integral to the popular image of a medical doctor as a white coat.

Coining the term stethoscope – from the Greek for chest (*stethos*) and to see (*skopein*) – Laënnec developed his amplifying paper tube into a robust wooden device. By the middle of the nineteenth century, it had been superseded by the familiar Y-shaped rubber tube with two earpieces.

⬚ Read

Duffin J. To See with a Better Eye: A life of RTH Laennec. New Jersey: Princeton University Press; 1998.

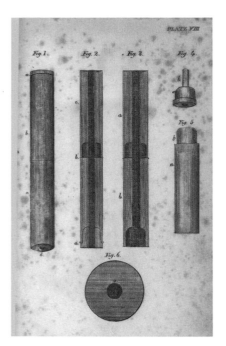

Laënnec's stethoscope
Engraving from *A Treatise on the Diseases of the Chest and on Mediate Auscultation*, 1829
René-Theophile-Hyacinthe Laënnec
L0033027 Wellcome Images

𝒪 The stethoscope paradox

While distancing the doctor from close physical contact, the stethoscope delivers intimate information about a patient's health. This new perspective was part of a general shift away from listening to patients' own descriptions of their ailments, and observing them closely, to a more objective study of physical symptoms.

As with any innovation, the stethoscope initially encountered resistance, with some physicians refusing to use the newfangled tool.

𝒪 Like hearing the grass grow

The stethoscope makes one of its first appearances in literature in George Eliot's *Middlemarch*, in the hands of Dr Lydgate, a forward-thinking newcomer treated with hostility by the locals. Set in 1829, the novel scrutinises human life while raising questions about the application of technology, as seen in this concern voiced by the narrator: 'If we have a keen vision and feeling of all ordinary human life, it would be like hearing the grass grow and the squirrel's heart beat, and we should die of that roar which lies on the other side of silence.'

BREATH

Wooden corbels
France, 17th–18th century

Face

The human face is a remarkably multipurpose tool. Contributing to the actions of looking, breathing, eating and talking, the face's muscles also express emotion, send out social signals, herald changes in health or well-being and reveal aspects of the inner self. For centuries, physicians have been taught to recognise structural and gestural changes in the face, which may act as diagnostic markers or measures of pain and discomfort.

The face is a symbol of its owner, a unique image recognisable to the self and others, even as it ages. Efforts to enhance, adorn or disguise the face range from applying cosmetics and accessories to much more interventionist techniques. The earliest surgical methods for reconstructing the face date back to at least the second millennium BCE. In the twenty-first century, the face transplant has become a reality, complete with attendant – but misguided – worries about taking on the identity of another.

Whether for aesthetic, entertaining or more sinister purposes, humans are avid observers of faces, seeking them out in inanimate objects and producing them in art, architecture and literature. Symmetrical, average faces usually elicit the most praise and adoration; different or damaged faces may attract discrimination or stigma. Under the historical scrutiny of physiognomic and phrenological analysis, or more contemporary facial-recognition systems, the make-up of your head and face might spell good or bad news for your relationship, your job or your freedom.

FACE

> ...we value [the face] not as a mere fixed form of beauty, which may remain like a bust before us, but as the varying index of the mind.
>
> Sir Charles Bell in *Essays on the Anatomy and Philosophy of Expression*, 1824

Wooden corbels

Wooden corbels
Oak
France, 17th–18th century
RRa0028–29 / A637147-8 Science Museum / L0075996 Wellcome Images

Before the thirteenth century, it was rare to find a frown or a smile in sculpture. Most heads in early art or architecture were representations of heroic or holy figures projecting serene impressions. In the Gothic era, facial expressions began to appear. Architectural 'marginalia', such as weight-supporting corbels, gave craftsmen opportunities to experiment with whimsical, cartoon-like personalities, which might lurk high up on the edges of monuments.

🖉 Beautiful and grotesque

On a visit to the ruins of Melrose Abbey in 1853, American writer Harriet Beecher Stowe (1811–96) wondered 'what gloomy, sarcastic, poetic, passionate mind' had recorded such fantastic faces on the fourteenth-century abbey's corbels, which she described as both beautiful and grotesque. 'One has the leer of fiendish triumph, with budding horns…' wrote Stowe in *Sunny Memories of Foreign Lands*, '…and then the gasping face of some old monk, apparently in the agonies of death, with his toothless gums, hollow cheeks, and sunken eyes. Other faces have an earthly and sensual leer; some are wrought into expressions of scorn and mockery, some of supplicating agony, and some of grim, despair.'

> One fancies each corbel to have had its history, its archetype in nature; a thousand possible stories spring into one's mind.
>
> Harriet Beecher Stowe in *Sunny Memories of Foreign Lands, Vol 1.*, 1854

📎 Spot Sir Henry

Henry Wellcome's profile is a key design motif used to bring character to furniture in the Reading Room. Henry's silhouette can be found in mouldings at the bases of plinths and cabinets, as a collar around the display tables and as a framing device in the cabinet vitrines and drawers.

To produce these shapes, a custom-made cutting tool was created by Reading Room architects AOC, based on the profile depicted in Hugh Goldwin Riviere's 1906 portrait of Wellcome. Aged 53 at the time, Wellcome was then married with a young son, and in sole charge of Burroughs Wellcome, a young, energetic and ground-breaking company.

Nothing is more common than to hear the study of physiognomy condemned as being calculated to mislead men in their judgments of each other, and the impossibility of its being reduced to a science; yet, nothing is more universally prevalent, in all classes of society, than forming judgments from the appearances of the face.

From *The Pocket Lavater, or, The Science of Physiognomy*, 1817

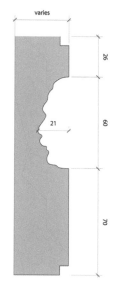

Henry Wellcome portrait, profile design drawing and steel-cutting tool
45866i Wellcome Library / AOC

📖 Read

Eco U. On Ugliness. London: Harvill Secker; 2007.
Little CT. Set in Stone: The face in medieval sculpture. New York: Metropolitan Museum of Modern Art; 2013.

📎 All-seeing Mussolini

In 1933, Renato Bertelli created a continuous profile sculpture of Italian dictator Benito Mussolini. Though alluding to the myth of Janus – the Roman god with two faces who could look into both the past and the future – Bertelli's sculpture of a then all-powerful man could, naturally, see in *all* directions.

The silhouette of the soul

Johann Caspar Lavater (1741–1801) valued the silhouette as the most useful physiognomic analysis tool. Unlike a portrait, a silhouette strips the body of emotion and fixes the pure, objective and 'incontrovertible' shape of the skull, which Lavater considered a direct expression of the soul.

**Silhouette
From *Essays on Physiognomy*,
late 18th century
Johann Caspar Lavater**
b12805154 Wellcome Library

**Charles Robert Darwin
Photograph
Julia Margaret Cameron, 1868**
12615i Wellcome Library

Darwin's listless nose

In his autobiography, Charles Darwin reported that the captain of HMS *Beagle*, Robert Fitzroy, almost rejected Darwin as a passenger due to the shape of his nose. Fitzroy was 'an ardent disciple of Lavater' and, said Darwin, '[he] was convinced that he could judge of a man's character by the outline of his features, and he doubted whether any one with my nose could possess sufficient energy and determination for the voyage'.

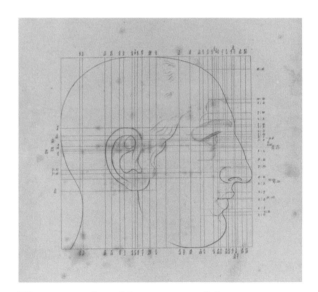

**The principles of harmony and beauty
From *Panharmonicon*, 1815
Francis Webb**
L0033915 Wellcome Images

FACE

Eagle-eyed

Just as Aristotle (384–322 BCE) did, many people can't resist linking individuals' characters with the animals their faces most resemble. Possessing an eagle's piercing gaze could represent a regal character, but it might also be seen as a sign of a cruel and predatory personality. Other birds have their own character traits: in *De Humana Physiognomia* (1586), Giambattista della Porta attributes a nose shaped like the beak of a raven or cock to a shameless and lecherous character.

Charles Le Brun (1619–90) systematised these instinctive hypotheses, dividing the faces of animals and humans into comparative segments. He concluded that a hooked nose, curved lips and large eyes indicated a grasping nature.

Every person with eyes in his own head has noticed the general resemblance which some of his fellow human beings bear to various animals – the lion, the ox, the goat, the horse, the fox, the cat, the monkey, the ass; and as for particular features and traits, such as the hawk or eagle nose...one cannot walk abroad without meeting with staring examples of them.

The London Literary Gazette and Journal of the Belles Lettres, Artes, Sciences Etc., No. 546, 1827

Relationship between the human face and that of the eagle
Lithograph from *Dissertation sur un Traité de Charles Le Brun*, 17th century
After Charles Le Brun
b12949048 Wellcome Library

The 'Visitorians'

In her 2012 book *You Animal, You!* artist and writer Charlotte Cory superimposed images of taxidermy animal heads on human photographic portraits from Victorian visiting cards. At first, Cory says, viewers find the subversive hybrid creatures she calls 'Visitorians' funny. The initial laughter then transforms into serious contemplation of these sometimes disturbing scenes.

Vegetable likenesses

Many facial characteristics have been likened to vegetables, from 'cherry lips' to 'potato noses' and 'cauliflower ears'. The sixteenth-century Italian painter Arcimboldo caricatured people as collages of vegetables, a method famously used by the *Sun* newspaper in 1992, when it gave ill-starred England football manager Graham Taylor a turnip for a head.

A carrot for a nose
Coloured lithograph
W Spooner, 19th century
11855i Wellcome Library

FACE

Interpreting expressions and complexions

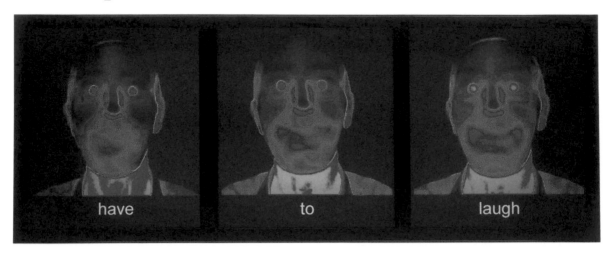

have   to   laugh

'Death Mask (Have to Laugh)'
Glass and plastic, duratrans
Ian Breakwell, 1998
C0069765 Wellcome Images

Multimedia artist Ian Breakwell (1943–2005) saw the face as 'a mere cowl', a mask constructed for the outside world. He likened this 'second skin' to a tight membrane that might be split by 'too broad a smile'. These thermal self-portraits show an alternative view of Breakwell's own skin, where the different colours represent varying surface temperatures.

Breakwell described his sense of humour as morose and deadpan, 'the seemingly unfunny stuff that is close to misery, but not quite.' He made this lightbox the same year as the collaborative artwork 'Death's Dance Floor', which was influenced by Hans Holbein's depiction of Death as a lively and mischievous figure. Breakwell faced death himself seven years later.

...it is scarcely possible to point out any difference between the tear-stained face of a person after a paroxysm of excessive laughter and after a bitter crying-fit.

Charles Darwin in *The Expression of the Emotions in Man and Animals*, 1872

A rose mask

After his diagnosis with cancer in 2004, Breakwell spent a feverish two weeks completing a series of works entitled 'Diagnosis Drawings'. One of the set's most striking pieces is a face constructed from blooming roses.

'Diagnosis Drawing'
Mixed media on paper
Ian Breakwell, 2005
Ian Breakwell / Anthony Reynolds Gallery, London

FACE

Complexion diagnosis

Inspecting the complexion is one of the four fundamental diagnostic approaches in traditional Chinese medicine. Practitioners study the colour of the face to identify bodily imbalances, classifying their observations according to five different phases: green–blue, red, yellow, white and black.

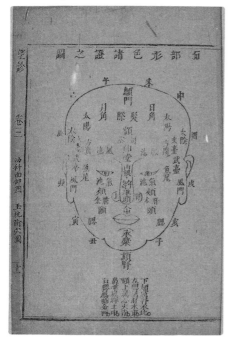

Paediatric complexion diagnosis chart
From *Sizhen Juewei*, 1726
Lin Zhihan
L0038677 Wellcome Images

Panicked passengers

Millions of dollars were spent deploying thermal-imaging face scanners in international airports during the 2003 outbreak of severe acute respiratory syndrome (SARS). The appeal of a speedy, non-contact tool for measuring the temperatures of thousands of passengers potentially suffering from fever is obvious, but the systems weren't designed for this purpose.

Thermal scanners only produce measurements relative to the surrounding area (not the absolute temperature of the individual) and their readings are only accurate if isolated from environmental fluctuations. Even then, passengers' skin temperatures might be raised by the consumption of alcohol or hot drinks, or by hormonal changes in the body; intense perspiration or heavy make-up can also cool the skin without affecting one's internal temperature.

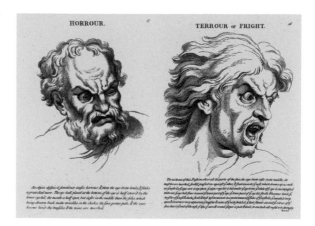

Horreur and Terrour or fright
From *Heads: Representing the various passions of the soul*, c.1760
Charles Le Brun
b1091450x Wellcome Library

The expression of the soul

In 1668, painter Charles Le Brun delivered a lecture on 'expression' to members of the Académie Royale de Peinture et de Sculpture. Le Brun argued that, due to its proximity to the soul, the face is the most expressive part of the body.

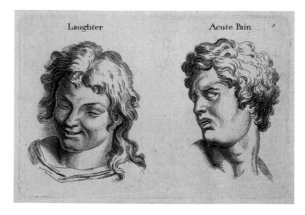

Laughter and Acute pain
Engraving
John Tinney after Charles Le Brun, *c.*1760
32372i Wellcome Library

Read

Cole J. About Face. Cambridge: MIT Press; 1997.
Darwin C, Ekman P. The Expression of the Emotions in Man and Animals. New York: Oxford University Press; 2009.

FACE

Life mask of Ludwig van Beethoven

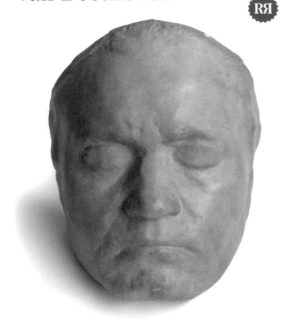

Life mask of Sir Henry Wellcome
Plaster
*c.*1902
L0044076 Wellcome Images

Death mask of James Bloomfield Rush

Life mask of Ludwig van Beethoven
Plaster
*c.*1812
RRa0032 / A61198 Science Museum /
L0076011 Wellcome Images

Anatomical sculptor Franz Klein (1779–1840) cast the original version of this mask from Beethoven (1770–1827) in 1812, when the German composer was 42. Used as a preliminary study for a bronze bust, the furrowed brow and pained appearance were described years later by poet Rainer Maria Rilke as 'that hard knot of the senses tightly drawn together'. The tortured look provided the basis for many Beethoven portraits, thereby contributing to his popular image as an intense, morose man with a troubled psyche.

Many people (including the Swedish writer August Strindberg) had a copy of the mask on their wall, erroneously believing it to have been made at the time of Beethoven's death.

🖉 An unaffected, real portrait

In his teens, fellow composer Richard Wagner (1813–83) commented on the impression Beethoven's 'physiognomy' made on him. Considering himself Beethoven's spiritual heir, he later commissioned a portrait of his hero. Wagner expressly requested that the image present the true, rather than ideal, Beethoven.

Death mask of James Bloomfield Rush
Paint on plaster
*c.*1849
RRa0030 / A127716 Science Museum /
L0076004 Wellcome Images

FACE

James Bloomfield Rush (1800–49) was convicted of one of the most infamous crimes of the nineteenth century: the murder of his landlord Isaac Jermy and attacks on Mrs Jermy and the couple's housemaid. Known as the 'Killer in the Fog', Rush was executed by hanging at Norwich Castle. An hour later, his body was taken down, his head shaved and his death mask cast.

'A headstrong horse'

Casts of criminals' heads allowed the study of the criminal personality using physiognomy and phrenology. The contemporary publication *The Stanfield Hall Assassinations! Authentic report of the trial, conviction and extraordinary defence of James Bloomfield Rush* included a phrenological examination of Rush's head:

> 'His forehead is small and low... altogether the front part of the head does not indicate any mental power... His forehead is narrow; ideality is very deficient, he has no great degree of imagination; his circle of mental vision is extremely limited. The top of his head is flat; benevolence and veneration are wanting; he has naturally no strong religious tendencies... That organ named destructiveness, is full above the ear, it ought to be called impulsiveness (that which prompts a man to immediate action)... He is naturally five times more animal than intellectual, and his whole history proves him to have been a gross sensualist – a man incapable of any generous emotion, a low, mean, grovelling character, but of active habits... a headstrong horse...'

The Chamber of Comparative Physiognomy

A wax image of Rush, 'taken from life at Norwich', was a star attraction at London's Madame Tussauds, where it was displayed in the gallery *Punch* nicknamed 'The Chamber of Horrors'. The room was later retitled 'The Chamber of Comparative Physiognomy', though this scientific-sounding title didn't stick. Rush had more staying power: his model remained on display for over a century.

Read

Crone R. Violent Victorians. Manchester: Manchester University Press; 2012.
Pilbeam P. Madame Tussaud: And the history of waxworks. London: Bloomsbury; 2006.

The telegraphed mugshot

Alphonse Bertillon (1853–1914) introduced the world's first scientific prisoner-identification system when working for the Paris police in the 1880s. Although daguerrotypes of prisoners had been taken since before Bertillon was born, there were no standard poses or lighting, and facial features were inconsistently described.

Bertillon introduced the familiar front and side 'mugshot' while also recording a number of other characteristics. Intending to produce a physical description that could be transmitted by telegraph, Bertillon noted the colour of eyes, hair and skin as well as measurements relating to the prisoner's height, the length of their fingers, head and feet and the shape of the ear. By 1899, 'Bertillonage' was used by police forces in over a dozen countries. However, while the mugshot persisted, Bertillon's multiple-measurement approach was short-lived. By the middle of the twentieth century it had been replaced by fingerprinting, a system less reliant on data likely to have been collected in many different ways.

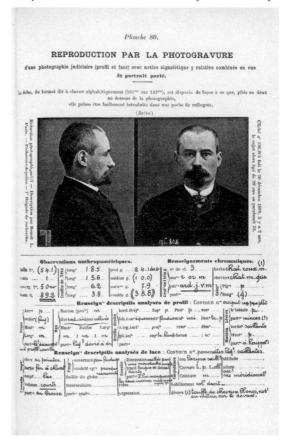

Alphonse Bertillon
From *Instructions Signalétiques Album*, 1893
L0076890 Wellcome Images

FACE

The perfect average

Victorian polymath and statistician Sir Francis Galton (1822–1911) explored the concept of facial beauty using photography. By combining portraits of different individuals, he produced composite images that might reveal their common features. In general, Galton found composite faces more beautiful than any individual face, stumbling upon the idea that perfection is essentially the average. Galton also applied his composite methods to 'distil' the typical look of the criminal from individual photographs of convicted felons. His results again tended to look like the law-abiding average.

Specimens of composite portraiture
From *Inquiries into Human Faculty and its Development*, 1883
Francis Galton
b12086514 Wellcome Library

Unromantic choices

In 1990, American psychologists Judith Langlois and Lori Roggman revisited Francis Galton's investigation into facial beauty, using computers to build their own composite images. Their results confirmed Galton's: both women and men were considered more attractive as composites, and the greater the number of individuals combined in a single image, the more attractive the result was judged to be. In discussing their unromantic finding – that we naturally tend to select partners with characteristics close to the mean – Langlois and Roggman apologised to readers of their scientific paper for such a 'parsimonious answer to the question of what constitutes beauty'.

> *I use this plan for my beauty data classifying the girls I passed in streets or elsewhere as attractive, indifferent, or repellent... I found London to rank highest for beauty; Aberdeen lowest.*
>
> Sir Francis Galton
> in *Memories of My Life*, 1909

Read

Ellenbogen J. Reasoned and Unreasoned Images: The photography of Bertillon, Galton and Marey. Pennsylvania: The Pennsylvania State University Press; 2012.

The wrong face

In the mid-sixteenth century, years after well-to-do peasant Martin Guerre left his Pyrenean village without explanation, a man was accepted as Guerre by his wife, child and fellow villagers. All ran smoothly for years, until Mrs Guerre took her 'husband' to court claiming he was an impostor. When the case was about to be resolved in the man's favour, the wife's story was proven by the reappearance of the real Martin Guerre.

This true tale may seem bizarre, even in a time pre-dating identity documents and photography, yet it remains unclear whether Mrs Guerre was a simple woman deceived by an impostor (as others were), or an abandoned parent happy to embrace the pretence offered by an alternative husband.

'Portrait of Mr J Kay, Afflicted with a Rodent Disease'

'Portrait of Mr J Kay, Afflicted with a Rodent Disease'
Oil on canvas
*c.***1820**
RRa0091 / 603117i Wellcome Library

The diagnosis of this disfigured man is unclear. The term 'rodent' is usually connected with cancer, and this painting includes the inscription 'cancer of the nose', but Mr Kay also has the distinctive look of someone with Hutchinson's teeth, a sign of congenital syphilis.

> A man without a nose [arouses] horror and loathing, and people are apt to regard the deformity as a just punishment for his sins. This division of diseases, or even more their consequences, into blameworthy and blameless is strange... As if all people with noses were always guiltless!

German surgeon
Johan Friedrich Dieffenback, 1834

Audiences watching the 1925 silent movie of the novel were said to faint at the moment when Lon Chaney (known as the 'Man of a Thousand Faces') removed his mask to reveal the grotesque sight beneath.

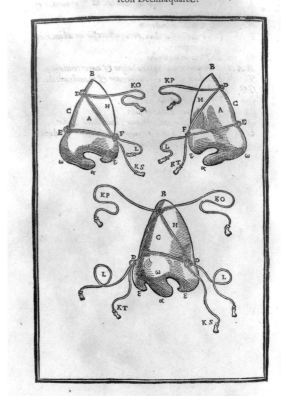

Covers for the nose
Woodcut from Gasparis Tagliacozzi's
De Curtorum Chirurgia, 1597
b13152191 Wellcome Library

The syphilitic nose

From the earliest syphilis epidemic in the sixteenth century, a sunken or missing nose was recognised as a sign of the disease. It also marked its owner (or their parents) as corrupt or dangerous. Facial surgeons in the nineteenth century performed reconstructive surgery in an effort to remove this stigma. Operating before antisepsis and anaesthesia, they and their patients were clearly willing to take risks in order to gain an almost human nose.

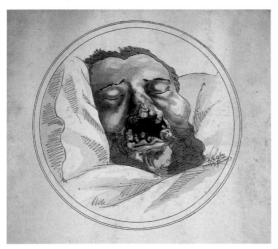

Eroded and gangrenous nasal cartilage due to syphilis
Watercolour
Alphonse Legros, 1885
576911i Wellcome Library

The Phantom's face

In his 1911 novel *Le Fantôme de l'Opéra (The Phantom of the Opera)*, Gaston Leroux describes the absence of his central character's nose as 'a horrible thing to look at'. Born with this horror, the Phantom's face is an unspoken sign of congenital syphilis.

> When he went out in the streets or ventured to show himself in public, he wore a pasteboard nose, with a mustache attached to it, instead of his own horrible hole of a nose. This did not quite take away his corpse-like air, but it made him almost, I say, almost endurable to look at.

From *The Phantom of the Opera*
by Gaston Leroux, 1911

FACE

🖉 Old new noses

Evidence of nasal reconstruction dates back to papyri from 1600 BCE, which describe methods for repairing a broken nose. Hindu surgeon Susrata (*c.*500 BCE) also refers to rhinoplasty in his *Susrata Samhita* encyclopedia.

The Indian method of rhinoplasty
From *An Account of Two Successful Operations for Restoring a Lost Nose...*, 1816
L0032285 Wellcome Images

In the sixteenth century, Gasparis Tagliacozzi (1546–99) experimented with using flaps of skin from other parts of the body, known as 'pedicles'. He shared his work in the first textbook on plastic surgery, *De Curtorum Chirurgia*.

Artificial nose
Plated metal
17th–18th century
L0058566 Wellcome Images / A641037 Science Museum

16th-century plastic surgery on the nose
From Gasparis Tagliacozzi's
***De Curtorum Chirurgia*, 1597**
b13152191 Wellcome Library

The barbarous process of Rhinoplasty consists not in restoring the original proboscis, but in manufacturing a wretched apology for it from two flaps of skin cut from the cheek.

'Phases of Physiognomy',
Manchester Times, 13 October 1866

📖 Read

Barnett R. The Sick Rose: Disease and the art of medical illustration. London: Thames & Hudson, 2014.

Gilman SL. Making the Body Beautiful: A cultural history of aesthetic surgery. New Jersey: Princeton University Press; 1999.

Leroux G. The Phantom of the Opera. London: Collins Classics; 2011.

FACE

Phrenological head

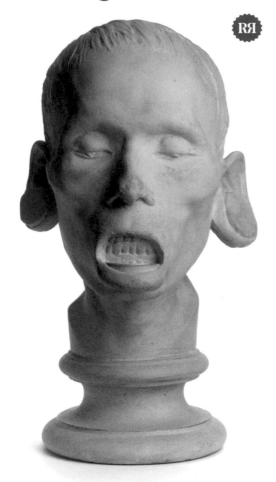

Phrenological head
O'Neill & Son Statuaries, Edinburgh
Phrenological Society, 1826
RRa0031 / A32960 Science Museum /
L0076007 Wellcome Images

This plaster cast of the head of a man from the Botocudos people of Brazil was made in Edinburgh, the principal British centre for phrenology in the nineteenth century.

⬚ Views of the Botocudos people

The name Botocudos comes from the Portuguese *botoque*, meaning 'plug', a reference to disks or plugs worn in the lips and ears. In 1853, French professor Henri Hollard described the features of the Botocudos people as 'broad and flat, with prominent brow, high cheekbones, small bridgeless nose, wide nostrils and slight projection of the jaws. They are longheaded, and their hair is coarse, black and lank'.

In the same year, George Combs's *A System of Phrenology* analysed the head of the 'Brazil Indian':

> *'The deficiency in Size is the same [as the 'full-blooded Indian'], indicating natural inferiority of mind, and the combination of organs is similar, only Firmness is not so great, and Concentrativeness and Philoprogenitiveness are moderate…*
> *The cast of the Brazil Indian shews a deficiency in size compared with the European; and hence it corresponds with the fact, that these Indians are regarded and treated as children, that they are destitute of foresight, and of that degree of steadiness of purpose which pursues a remote advantage through numerous intervening obstacles.'*

⬚ Feeling lumps and bumps

Phrenology – from the Greek *phren* (mind) and *logos* (knowledge) – interprets a person's character by 'reading' the shape of their skull. The practice emerged in eighteenth-century Vienna and was pioneered by German physician Franz Joseph Gall (1758–1828), who called his approach 'cranioscopy'. Gall thought the development of the brain's 27 inner senses determined the shape of the brain and therefore the shape of the surrounding bone.

Based on straightforward guiding principles, and requiring only an interpretative map, phrenology could be practised by anyone. By the middle of the nineteenth century it was a popular self-improvement tool, used on oneself, one's children or one's servants in order to understand and overcome inherent characteristics.

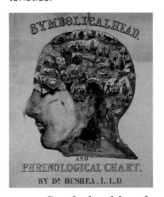

LEFT: **Symbolical head**
Coloured wood engraving
After O S Fowler, *c.*1845
27921i Wellcome Library

RIGHT: **Hudson's Soap advertisement**
Diecut card
R S Hudson Ltd., *c.*1910
b16632722 Wellcome Library

FACE

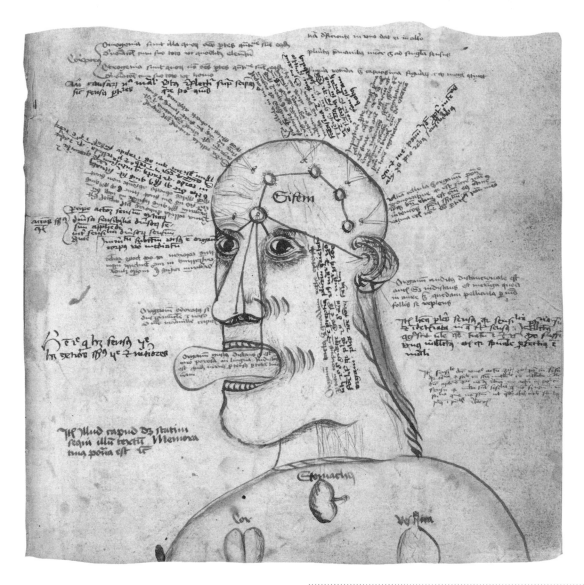

**Pen drawing of localised 'cell' interpretation
of mental activity
Johann Lindner after Aristotle, 1472–74**
L0044182 Wellcome Images

🖉 Localised brain functions

The long-held belief that brain functions were local-ised in different areas was ultimately proven by Paul Broca (1824–80), who discovered 'Broca's area', the part of the brain related to speech, in 1861.

📖 Read

Clarke E et al. An Illustrated History of Brain Func-tion: Imaging the brain from antiquity to the present. San Francisco: Norman Publishing; 1996.

🖉 *Travels in Phrenologasto*

In his 1825 book *Travels in Phrenologasto*, John Trotter (writing as Don Jose Blascopo) describes how he is blown off course when travelling by hot-air balloon and discovers a race of people who 'all wore their hair very closely shaven, and had their heads painted white'. What's more, 'the head of every indi-vidual was chalked out by black lines into a variety of little fields and enclosures.'

Blascopo soon learns that when a Phrenologasto boy reaches his 16th birthday, his head is shaven in a formal ceremony during which doctors divide the skull into 33 different compartments and mark the predominant characteristic with a red-hot iron. The traveller willingly subjects himself to this ritual only to be categorised as 'unmarked by any rare talent, virtue or disposition' and identified as showing 'symptoms of imbecility'. Blascopo is astonished and mortified by this very public loss of face.

'A Blacksmith Extracting a Tooth'
18th century

Pain

Pain is a universal human experience, but an extremely diverse one. How individuals cope with, express and share information about pain differs from person to person and culture to culture. The experience of pain also has a psychological component: the mind may locate pain in parts of the body that don't exist or block out memories of pain that has been endured.

In ancient times, pain wasn't a sense, symptom or signal, but a condition in itself. Ironically, the medical remedies designed to treat it – such as bleeding, blistering or purging – were more likely to cause pain than alleviate it. Centuries later, some surgeons relied on cries of pain to help guide operations, or recommended physical suffering as an integral part of the recovery process.

Deriving from the Latin *poena*, meaning 'penalty', pain may also be a punishment, inflicted – by the self, other humans or divine beings – as penance for wrongdoing or past sins. In the Christian tradition, the labour pains of all women are a chastisement for Eve's bite of forbidden fruit in the Garden of Eden and a humble reminder of the sinful state of humankind.

While the quest to conquer pain has driven the development of effective analgesics and anaesthetics, providing or using pain relief can be a culturally and politically charged issue. Demands for access to effective pain treatments also prompt questions about the level of control patients may relinquish in return for respite.

PAIN

It is evidently impossible to transmit the impression of pain by teaching, since it is only known to those who have experienced it. Moreover, we are ignorant of each type of pain before we have felt it.

Galen, 2nd century

'A Blacksmith Extracting a Tooth'

'A Blacksmith Extracting a Tooth'
Oil on canvas
In the manner of John Collier
(known as 'Tim Bobbin'), 18th century
RRa0094 / 44637i Wellcome Library

In the eighteenth century, teeth were cleaned and pulled by blacksmiths, tooth-drawers, barbers and barber-surgeons. Each of these might generate additional income by selling pain-relieving remedies, but they weren't the only traders who cashed in on toothache; diarist James Boswell (1740–95) documented buying a tooth tincture from a London bookseller.

Years ago the blacksmith's forge was the recognised dentistry, and even now one often meets aged folk in out-of-the-way places who can recall having teeth extracted in the village smithy. The idea may seem very quaint to-day, although many people daily submit themselves to tooth-pullers who have even fewer qualifications than the blacksmith had. The result is that many people who have failed in other directions feel they have a bent for dental surgery.

The *Warwick Advertiser*, 1914

Tri-Dent dental station

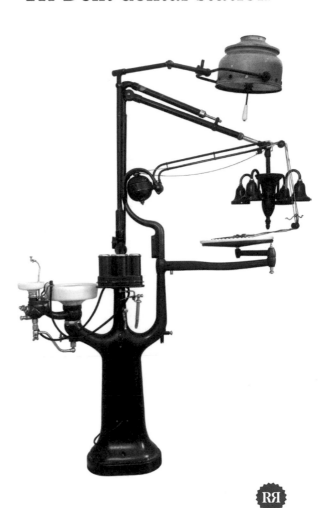

A barber's chair modified for dental extractions
English ash and elm
18th century
1981-2215 Science Museum / L0065953 Wellcome Images

Tri-Dent dental station
Metal, glass and ceramic
Ritter Dental Manufacturing
Company Inc., *c*.1920
RRa0071 / L0075792 Wellcome Images

The Ritter Dental Manufacturing Company pioneered the grouping of dental operating tools within a single unit. Air, gas, water and electricity were all close to hand, along with a high-speed electric drill, a directional light and a fountain spittoon.

This station was developed around the time that the 1921 Dentists Act forced anyone practising dentistry in the UK to register with the General Medical Council. Unqualified dentists were still allowed to work so long as they were over the age of 23, could demonstrate good character and had practised as a dentist for five of the seven preceding years.

PAIN

REALLY PAINLESS EXTRACTIONS

A Set of Teeth from
£1 1s.

Really
Painless Extractions
2/6

Hours - 10 to 8
Saturdays till 2

Mr. SMEDLEY'S
Dental Surgery.

39, Beauchamp Place,
BROMPTON ROAD (near HARRODS),
LONDON, S.W.
AND AT
27, Grand Parade, Brighton

YEARS ago, when the need for more humane extractions first began to be realised, methods which merely reduced the pain were described as "Painless." Naturally this led to dissatisfaction and disbelief in all such things, but nowadays really painless extractions are being made every day. By our method nothing is felt which can be termed pain, and all nervous people should avail themselves of it.

COPYRIGHT

**Advertisement for Mr Smedley's
Dental Surgery
1913**
L0040514 Wellcome Images

Ø Dentophobia

Research studies suggest that fear of going to the dentist is a learned condition, related to previous experiences in the dentist's chair. Dentophobia therefore has more in common with post-traumatic stress disorder than other irrational fears.

American president Abraham Lincoln is said to have developed a fear of going to the dentist after undergoing a botched tooth extraction in 1841. When the statesman needed another tooth removed two decades later, he allegedly popped a container of chloroform out of his pocket and inhaled deeply before allowing the dentist to start work.

Mole paws used to protect against toothache
RRa0158 / 1985.51.361 Pitt Rivers Museum

Torture and hilarity

Undoubtedly the most excruciating scene of 'dentistry' committed to film is to be found in *Marathon Man* (1976), where Laurence Olivier uses a dental drill as an instrument of torture on Dustin Hoffman, spawning the oft-repeated quotation, 'Is it safe?' The same year, a more comic dental depiction featured in *The Pink Panther Strikes Again*, in which Inspector Clouseau disguises himself as a dentist to gain access to Inspector Dreyfus, who has excruciating toothache. Before attempting the extraction, Clouseau inhales and then administers laughing gas to his patient. As both collapse in hysterical laughter, Clouseau erroneously extracts a healthy tooth.

Read

Wynbrandt J. The Excruciating History of Dentistry: Toothsome tales and oral oddities from Babylon to braces. New York: St Martin's Press; 1998.

'The First Use of Ether as an Anaesthetic in Dental Surgery'

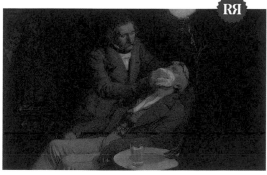

'The First Use of Ether as an Anaesthetic in Dental Surgery'
Oil on canvas
Ernest Board, *c*.1912
RRa0011 / 45904i Wellcome Library

American dentist William T G Morton (1819–68) experimented on a goldfish, a hen, his dog and himself, before offering $5 to any patient willing to become temporarily unconscious by inhaling ether vapour in 1846. Toothache-stricken Eben Frost took up the offer and documented the results immediately afterward: 'I did not experience the slightest pain whatever… and felt no unpleasant effects from the operation'.

Oh, what delight for every feeling heart to find the new year ushered in with the announcement of this noble discovery of the power to still the sense of pain, and veil the eye and memory from all the horrors of an operation. We have conquered pain!

Report on the use of ether as an anaesthetic in *People's Journal*, London, 1847

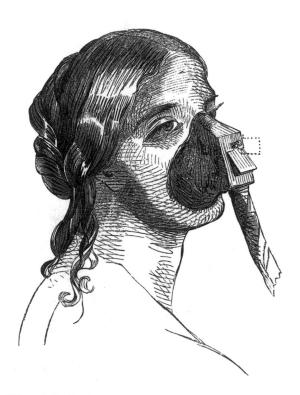

Ether inhalation apparatus
From *On the Inhalation of the Vapour of Ether in Surgical Operations*, 1847
John Snow
b14666339 Wellcome Library

The ether controversy

Despite the known efforts of others, William Morton asserted that he alone had conquered pain, even appealing to the US president to support his claim as sole discoverer of anaesthesia. Yet, as far back as 1799, Humphrey Davy had suggested using inhaled gas as an anaesthetic, and Morton's own former partner had used nitrous oxide before him – though his attempts to demonstrate it in public backfired when his patient ended up screaming. Surgeon Crawford Long had also conducted earlier experiments with ether, and scientist Charles Jackson even suggested to Morton the idea of using the vapour.

Anaesthesia before ether

The earliest use of a general anaesthetic predates William Morton by at least four decades. Japanese physician Seishu Hanaoka (1760–1835), a specialist in breast cancer, developed a combination of herbs based on traditional Chinese medicine. This was in use by 1804. Depending on the mixture, which included atropine and scopolamine, the patient was knocked out for between six and 24 hours.

Removing a cancerous growth from a woman's breast
From *Geka Kihai*, 1851
Kamata Keishu
L0031455 Wellcome Images

🗍 Read

Jay M. Emperors of Dreams: Drugs in the nineteenth century. Cambridgeshire: Dedalus; 2011.
Snow S. Blessed Days of Anaesthesia: How anaesthetics changed the world. Oxford: Oxford University Press; 2008.
Moscoso J. Pain: A cultural history. Basingstoke: Palgrave Macmillan; 2012.

When the dreadful steel was plunged into the breast... I began a scream that lasted unremittingly during the whole time of the incision – & I almost marvel that it rings not in my Ears still! So excruciating was the agony. When the wound was made, & the instrument was withdrawn, the pain seemed undiminished, for the air that suddenly rushed into those delicate edges felt like a mass of minute but sharp & forked poniards, that were tearing the edges of the wound.

Fanny Burney describing her unanaesthetised experience of breast-cancer surgery, 1811

Mesmer's successor

Ether was quickly taken up as a replacement for mesmerism (see p. 146), a technique that also produced an anaesthetic state. Unlike mesmerism, where the ability to enter a trance rested on establishing a rapport with the patient (which might take many consultations), inhalation of ether delivered rapid results. It also placed control of the situation firmly in the hands of the surgeon and his equipment.

Hurrah! Rejoice! Mesmerism, and its professors, have met with a heavy blow, and great discouragement. An American dentist has used ether...to destroy sensation in his operations, and the plan has succeeded...

Robert Liston, Professor of Surgery at University College Hospital, writing in 1847

Accidental awareness

Wakefulness during general anaesthesia is a common fear for pre-operative surgical patients. The phenomenon is a central plot device in the 2007 film *Awake*, in which Clay Beresford remains conscious but paralysed during his heart transplant. This allows him to hear that his surgeon intends to poison the donor heart and thus cause his body to reject it. As if that isn't bad enough, his new wife is in on the plot.

'A Homebirth'

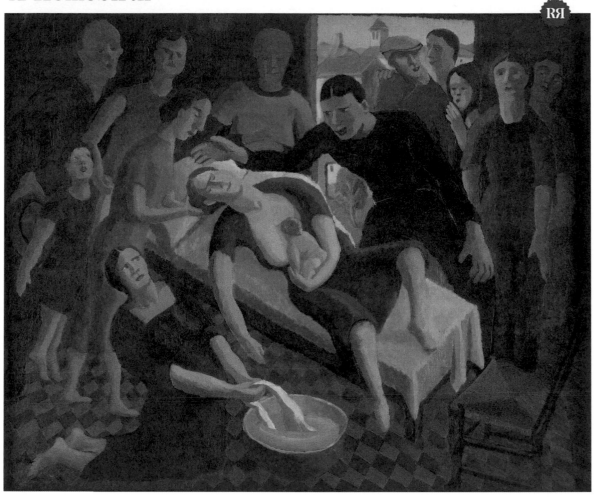

'A Homebirth'
Oil on canvas
Karl Hagedorn, c.1950
RRa0092 / 535949i Wellcome Library

German-born painter Karl Hagedorn (1889–1969) depicts childbirth as a public home-based event rather than a controlled hospital experience. Though this had been the norm for centuries, the 1954 *Report on the Obstetric Service under the National Health Service* recommended that all UK births should take place in institutions for 'maximum safety for mother and child'.

A birth is deemed natural, when it comes on in forty Weeks from the Time of Conception, and the Infant is born by the Force of Pains...

Physician and man midwife Brudenell Exton in *A New and General System of Midwifery*, 1753

⬙ Midwives, whether female or male

Laying a good claim to being the world's oldest profession, midwifery was integral to childbirth in ancient Rome, with women attending the birth unless labour was particularly difficult. According to Soranus of Ephesus (second century CE), a good midwife should be respectable and literate, with good wit and memory. They ought to love their work, possess a sympathetic disposition and be endowed with long slim fingers and short nails.

Women prevailed in the field until the early eighteenth century, when male midwives who had received training in modern anatomy started competing for birth business. Their arrival led to a more formally educated and technological approach, in which female midwives could be dismissed as unenlightened.

**A maid giving sweetmeats to gossips
in a birth room
17th century**
L0019348 Wellcome Images

*A drink sprinkled with powdered
sow's dung will relieve
the pains of labour, as will sow's
milk mixed with honey wine.*

Pliny the Elder, 1st century

📎 Gossips

Until the last century, birth was a social occasion,
which took place at home in the presence of friends
and family. The attendant women assisted in the birth,
cared for mother and baby and also tended to the
home and the husband. These 'sisters-in-God', who
chattered throughout the mother's labour, became
known as 'God-sibs', or 'gossips'.

In modern-day Scientology, mothers – and anyone else present – are forbidden from making noise
during the birth. Any screams of pain are thought
to negatively affect the child.

**Birthing scene
Marble
Ostia, Italy, 400 BCE–300 CE**
A129245 Science Museum / L0065025 Wellcome Images

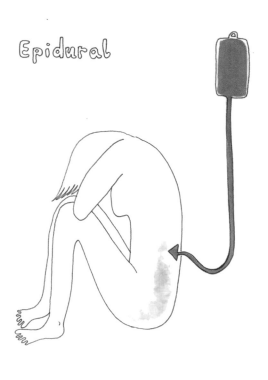

Epidural

'Epidural Anaesthesia'
Illustration
Mary Rouncefield, 2013
B0009517 Wellcome Images

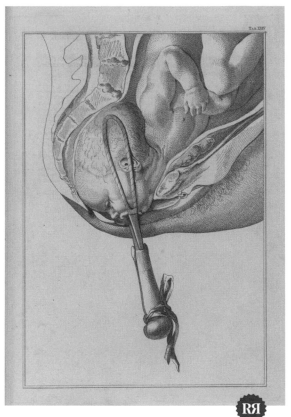

Forceps delivery
From William Smellie's *A Sett of Anatomical Tables with Explanations*, 1754
RRd0192 / b1297130 Wellcome Library

Erasing the memory of pain

Popular at the start of the twentieth century, 'twilight sleep' was a combination of scopolamine and morphine used during labour and delivery. The drug cocktail induced a semiconscious state and, rather than removing pain, removed the memory of it, with 60 to 70 per cent of mothers unable to recall any labour pain.

Twilight sleep briefly became the labour-drug of choice for high-society women, but was never used universally due to the need for constant supervision; physical restraints and protection for the mother; and the transmission of narcotics to the baby. However, the twilight sleep fad sparked a campaign for women to be able to choose their method of pain relief – even if that choice meant surrendering control of the birth to medical staff.

Alien labour

Mainstream depictions of childbirth tend to connect labour pain with danger, the possibility of death and, in many horror films, the arrival of supernatural or satanic creatures. Powerful imagery of childbirth (as well as the female and male reproductive systems) saturates the *Alien* films (1979–97), most memorably in the 'chestburster' scene in which the alien explodes from the thorax of the male character, Kane.

PAIN

Read

Cassidy T. Birth: A history. London: Chatto & Windus; 2007.

Epstein RH. Get Me Out: A history of childbirth from the Garden of Eden to the sperm bank. New York: Norton; 2011.

Acupuncture models

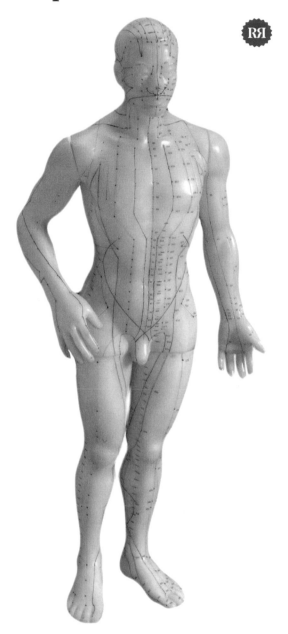

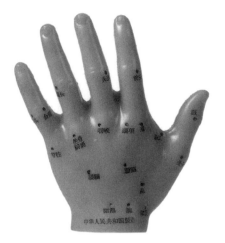

Acupuncture hand
Plastic
China, *c.*1970
RRa0108 / L0076295 Wellcome Images

Acupuncture figure
Plastic
China, *c.*1970
RRa0306 / A604025 Science Museum /
L0057959 Wellcome Images

In traditional Chinese medicine, acupuncture models illustrate points where sharp needles are inserted into the skin to promote the circulation of *qi*. Often located at a distance from the observed medical symptoms, these positions are understood to mark locations where the body's internal network of channels reaches the surface.

The heart channel of the arm
Painting from *Renti Jingmai Tu (Illustrations of the Channels of the Human Body)*
1662–1722
L0039967 Wellcome Images

PAIN

The bronze men

In the eleventh century, Wang Weiyi (*c*.987–1067) cast two life-sized human figures from bronze, each of which included over 650 holes at acupuncture points. When covered with wax and filled with water, the models were used as teaching aids. Students who correctly located an acupuncture position were rewarded by water released as their needle penetrated the wax. Weiyi also published an illustrated guide for those unable to use his models.

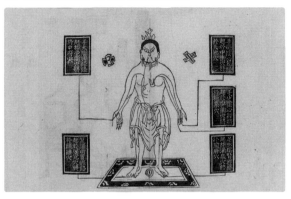

Heart, lung and stomach channels
Woodcut from *Bu Zhu Tongren*
***Shuxue Zhenjiu Tujing*, 1909**
Wang Weiyi
L0037946 Wellcome Images

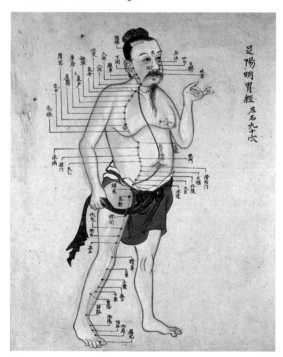

Acupuncture chart
Watercolour
18th century
567656i Wellcome Library

'A proper remedy'

Although acupuncture became known to the West in the seventeenth century, the first English text describing the practice was *A Treatise on Acupuncturation* (1823) by James Morss Churchill. The book reports several cases where acupuncture delivered pain relief to rheumatism sufferers who had not been helped by blistering or cupping.

Two years later, Benjamin Franklin's great-grandson, the physician and chemist Franklin Bache (1792–1864), experimented with acupuncture on prisoners at the state penitentiary in Philadelphia. He concluded that the technique had 'remarkable power'.

So far as I can judge from my limited experience, my impression is, that acupuncturation possesses a remarkable power in removing and mitigating pain. This agency... points to it as a proper remedy in almost all diseases, whose prominent symptom is pain.

Franklin Bache reporting his results in the
North American Medical Surgery Journal, 1826

The renaissance of acupuncture

Despite being practised for several thousand years, acupuncture was banned in nineteenth-century China – by a Chinese government keen on modernising medicine – and the technique was dropped from the curriculum of the Imperial Medical Academy. After the establishment of the People's Republic of China in 1949, traditional medicine was once again encouraged, accompanied by investment in new colleges of traditional Chinese medicine.

Read

Bivins R. Alternative Medicine? A history. Oxford: Oxford University Press; 2007.

Eckman P. In the Footsteps of the Yellow Emperor: Tracing the history of traditional acupuncture. California: Long River Press; 2007.

Kaptchuk TJ. The Web that has no Weaver: Understanding Chinese medicine. London: Random House; 2000.

PAIN

Carved wooden figure of Job

RЯ

Carved wooden figure of Job
Germany?, 1750–1850
RRa0107 / A637849 Science Museum /
L0076056 Wellcome Images

The biblical story of Job reflects on the nature of
suffering and the perennial question of why bad
things happen to good people. Although Job's friends
think his physical and emotional pain must surely be
punishment for some sinful deed, his boils and sores
are actually part of an experiment hatched between
God and Satan.

When Satan wagers Job's moral fibre would fall
away if he no longer had a life of such wealth and
comfort, God allows the devil to inflict a series of mis-
fortunes on his loyal servant. Through it all, even after
losing all his worldly possessions and suffering the
deaths of his children, Job continues to worship God.

'The deadly fruit of original sin'

Before disfigured Joseph Merrick (1862–90) moved
into the London Hospital, the 'Elephant Man' was
displayed in a vacant grocer's shop opposite, billed
as 'the deadly fruit of original sin'.

Joseph Merrick
Engraving
***British Medical Journal*, 1886**
L0026215 Wellcome Images

Read

Bourke J. The Story of Pain: From prayer to painkillers.
    Oxford: Oxford University Press; 2014.
Cohen E. The Modulated Scream: Pain in late medi-
    eval culture. Chicago: Chicago University Press;
    2010.
Lewis CS. The Problem of Pain. London: Harper
    Collins; 2002.

Suffering en route to enlightenment

One of the most important figures in Tibetan Bud-
dhism, the poet and adept Milarepa, was obliged to
endure years of suffering to expiate youthful sins and
reach enlightenment. Milarepa became the disciple
of the Buddhist master Marpa, who made him work
as a manual labourer. He was subjected to various

ordeals, violence and abuse before Marpa transmitted to him the spiritual teachings leading to Vajradhara, or complete enlightenment.

'Lord Milarepa's hundred thousand songs...'
L0025571 Wellcome Images

⬛ Penitent pain

Worn around the thigh, the metal teeth on this leather belt inflicted pain on its Christian wearer as a form of penance for their sins.

Penance belt
Leather and metal
Europe, 15th–16th century
A135381 Science Museum / L0057586 Wellcome Images

⬛ Trial by ordeal

In medieval times, painful physical trials were part of the judicial process. The accused might be commanded to carry a red-hot iron poker for nine feet, plunge their arm into a pot of boiling water or be thrown into deep, cold water.

2.ᵉ Epreuve de l'Eau froide

The cold-water ordeal
Etching with engraving
43313i Wellcome Library

> *The third way [of exterior penance] is to chastise the body, that is, to inflict pain on it, by wearing hairshirts, cords, or iron chains; by scourging or wounding oneself; and by similar austerities.*
>
> Saint Ignatius of Loyola
> in *Spiritual Exercises*, 16th century

PAIN

Statue of Saint Livertin

RR

Statue of Saint Livertin
Carved and painted wood
France, 1500–1750
RRa0027 / A634582 Science Museum /
L0076308 Wellcome Images

The ill-documented Saint Livertin is a patron saint
of headaches. In the Christian faith, praying to him
is thought to alleviate the pain and suffering of
headaches.

✐ 'Superfluity of excrements'

In his 1632 medical manual *Praxis Medicinae*, Gual-
terus Bruele describes headache as 'a painefull grief
of the head, by reason of some dangerous and sad
change thereof'. Bruele considered the head to be
'more tormented with paine then any other parte of
the body', a state caused by the assault of vapours
and swelling humours ascending from the body
below. Bruele also blamed the cold and moist brain,
and the 'superfluity of excrements' within it, which
would 'disturbe the head with aches'.

✐ The golden headband

Headaches are used as a form of magical punishment in the 1970s cult Japanese TV series *Saiyuki
(Monkey)* and the sixteenth-century Chinese novel
on which it is based, Wu Cheng'en's *Journey to the
West*. The titular character, Monkey, who becomes
protector to the monk Tripitaka to atone for earlier
sins, has his wayward behaviour controlled by a magical golden headband. Whenever Monkey strays out of
line, Tripitaka recites a special sutra that makes the
band contract, causing unbearably painful headaches.

**Advertisement for an electropathic
belt to treat neuralgia
The Medical Battery Co. Ltd.,** *c.*1893
b16768413 Wellcome Library

✐ Lost for words

Describing the pain of headaches has proved a challenge for even the most eloquent writers. Virginia
Woolf wrote in *On Being Ill* that 'English, which can
express the thoughts of Hamlet and the tragedy
of Lear, has no words for the shiver and the headache…' Emily Dickinson, who suffered from migraine
attacks, described the experience in one poem as
a 'Funeral in my brain', with mourners treading about
in 'boots of lead'.

📖 Read

Eadie MJ. Headache: Through the centuries. Oxford:
    Oxford University Press; 2012.

PAIN

Demons and drills

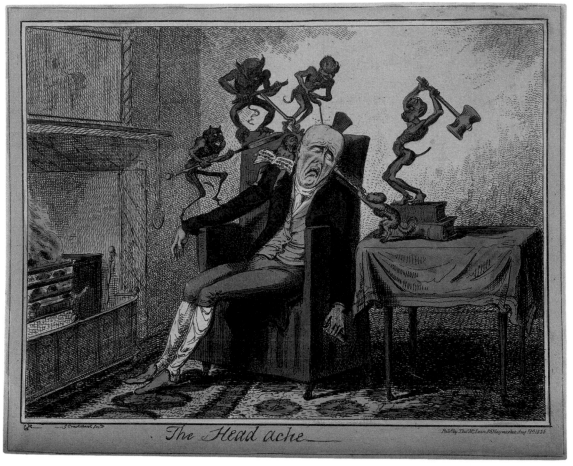

The Head ache

'The Head Ache'
Etching with watercolour
G Cruikshank after Captain F Marryat, 1835
869i Wellcome Library

In many cultures, headaches have been attributed to the presence of evil spirits or humours, with treatments designed to help these troublesome interferences escape from the body.

RIGHT: Removing the bone after trephination
Woodcut from *Feldtbuch*
***der Wundartzney*, 1530**
Hans von Gersdorff
RRd0181 / b10326492 Wellcome Library

Trephination or trepanation (see p.154) is one of many approaches that have been used to relieve the pressure and tension of headache pain. Other remedies include blistering, bloodletting and electric shocks administered by laying an electric torpedo fish across the brow.

'Saint Cosmas and Saint Damian Dressing a Chest Wound'

**'Saint Cosmas and Saint Damian
Dressing a Chest Wound'
Oil on canvas
Antonie de Favray, 1748**
RRa0016 / 44856i Wellcome Library

Third-century Christian physicians Cosmas and
Damian are considered patron saints of physicians
and pharmacists. Said to practise medicine without
charging fees, the twin brothers' miraculous healing
powers became legendary after their martyrdom, with
images and stories about their work appearing for
many centuries.

✐ The painless leg graft

One Cosmas and Damian miracle story that became
popular in the thirteenth century involved the saints
appearing to a sick man in a church in Rome. After
undergoing the amputation of his diseased leg, and
receiving a graft from an Ethiopian corpse, the patient
was said to feel no pain.

**'A Verger's Dream'
Oil on wood
Master of Los Balbases, *c*.1495**
46009i Wellcome Library

What makes a miracle?

In the 1730s, soon-to-be Pope Prospero Lambertini (1675–1758) formalised five criteria for diagnosing a miracle. To qualify, an event had to be:

1. Caused by the actions of a candidate for sainthood.
2. Unexplained by science.
3. Documented by submitted evidence.
4. Verified by independent witnesses.
5. Approved by a Vatican committee of physicians.

Over 900 years of caring

Artist Antonie de Favray (1706–98) was a member of the Christian Order of St John, a community that built a church, convent and hospital in eleventh century Jerusalem. In later centuries, the order moved to Cyprus, Rhodes, Malta and Rome.

Hospital of the Knights of St John, Rhodes
Photograph
Istituto Storico-Archeologico di Rodi, 1931
662447i Wellcome Library

To palliate

In Samuel Johnson's 1755 dictionary, the verb 'palliate' is given several definitions. Along with 'to clothe' and 'to cover', it is described as 'to cure imperfectly or temporarily, not radically; to ease, not cure'. Centuries later, the World Health Organization cited pain control as a paramount component of 'palliative care', the 'total care of patients whose disease is not responsive to curative treatment', along with psychological, social and spiritual problems.

Praying not healing

Medieval hospitals (from the Latin *hospis*, meaning 'host' or 'guest') attached to priories and monasteries tended to focus more on caring than healing. While being fed, clothed and sheltered, the sick, hungry or poor inmates were expected to take communion, attend confession and join in prayers for their salvation. They might therefore find meaning and consolation in their suffering.

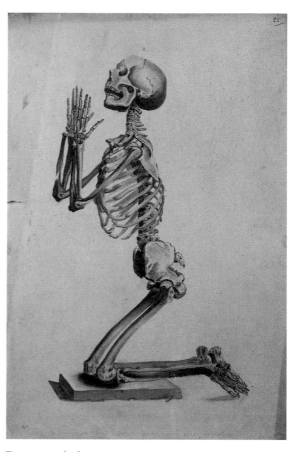

Praying skeleton
Ink and watercolour
After William Chesleden, *c*.1733
562970i Wellcome Library

Read

Duffin J. Medical Miracles: Doctors, saints and healing in the modern world. New York: Oxford University Press; 2009.

Duffin J. Medical Saints: Cosmas and Damian in a postmodern world. New York: Oxford University Press; 2013.

PAIN

'The Sense of Touch'

PAIN

'The Sense of Touch'
Oil on canvas
Lucas Franchoys the Younger, 17th century
RRa0093 / 45011i Wellcome Library

The seventeenth century was a period of intense philosophical exploration about the nature of the five senses, prompting many artists to try and reveal these phenomena. The link Lucas Franchoys the Younger makes between touch and pain is consistent with the association made by Cesare Ripa (c.1560–c.1623) in his influential dictionary for artists, *Iconologia* (1593). Iconography of the time also depicted 'touch' as a woman being bitten by a wild animal.

Read

Bacci F, Melcher D. Art and the Senses. Oxford: Oxford University Press; 2011.

Jütte R. A History of the Senses: From antiquity to cyberspace. Cambridge: Polity; 2005.

Kahlo F. The Diary of Frida Kahlo: An intimate self-portrait. New York: Abrams Books; 1995.

Wall P. Pain: The science of suffering. New York: Columbia University Press; 2000.

The face of pain

One of many different tools for measuring the intangible quality of pain, the 'FACES' scale prompts patients to choose which of six faces (from happy to tearful) represents their pain. However, watching a patient's own face might provide a more accurate measure, since a facial expression is an automatic reflex, not a considered or controlled response. The telltale signs of acute pain are thought to be lowering of the brows, tightening around closed or narrow eyes, a wrinkled nose and a raised upper lip. The mouth may also be stretched open, with a pull at the corner of the lips.

A painful plaster

The man in the painting opposite appears to be peeling a plaster or poultice from his arm. These pastes of herbs, oils, resins and wax were spread upon a cloth before being applied to the skin. Ingredients such as mustard seed might be added to deliberately cause blistering. Intended to draw out the bad humours thought to be causing the problem, these counterirritant mustard plasters may actually have aided healing by increasing blood flow.

Drug jar for mustard
Tin-glazed earthenware
Sicily, 16th–17th century
A42579 Science Museum / L0057152 Wellcome Images

'The Broken Column'

Mexican artist Frida Kahlo (1907–54) depicted the chronic pain she endured as a result of a series of spinal operations in a number of anguished works.

In 'The Broken Column' (1944), painted shortly after spinal surgery, Kahlo is shown split in half, her body peppered with protruding nails like a modern-day Saint Sebastian.

On pain of death

In Stieg Larsson's (1954–2004) *Millennium Trilogy*, the character Ronald Niedermann is congenitally unable to feel pain. The obvious dangers of such a condition are initially subverted in Niedermann's character, who gains advantage through his invulnerability to pain. However, when Lisbeth Salander immobilises him with a nail gun, his insensitivity to pain leads to his death.

A bird's beak piercing a woman's hand
Engraving
After George Glover, 17th century
27049i Wellcome Library

In using the term 'sense of pain',
I wish to be understood as
speaking of a sense apart from
that of touch or feeling.

George Augustus Rowell in *An Essay*
on the Beneficient Distribution
of the Sense of Pain, 1857

PAIN

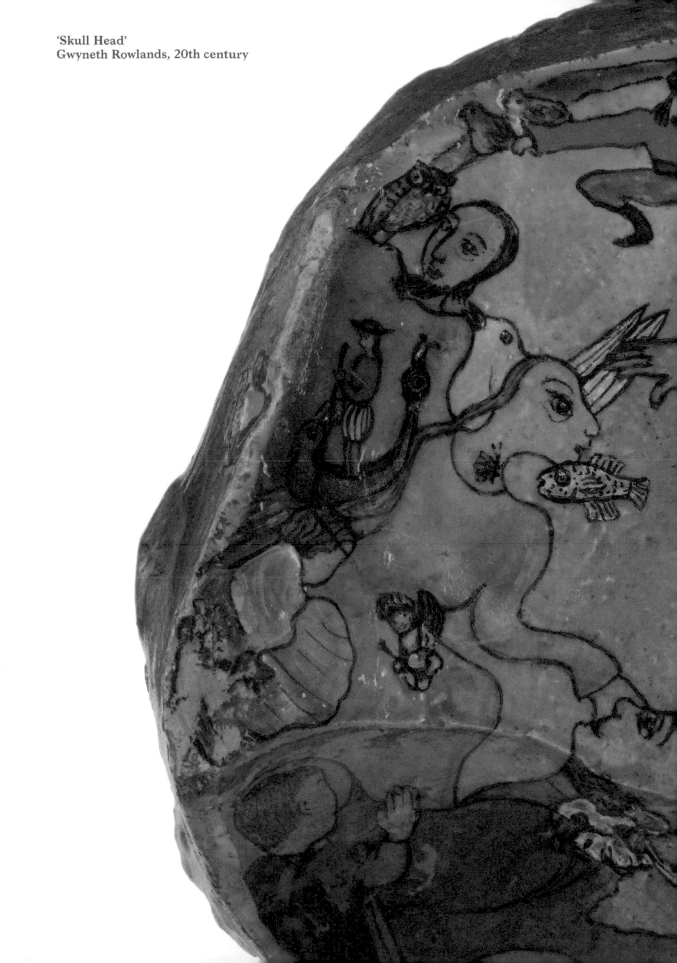

'Skull Head'
Gwyneth Rowlands, 20th century

Mind

The relationship between mind and body has kept Western philosophers occupied for millennia. While Plato argued that the seat of reason and knowledge was a distinct entity from the physical body, Aristotle disagreed. Centuries later, French philosopher René Descartes's dualistic model positioned the rational, free will that enables voluntary actions as a separate entity from the machine-like body, which drives automatic reflexes.

Views concerning what constitutes a 'normal' mind, and how, or if, unsound minds might be treated, have also changed across time. Traditionally, those considered to be insane, idiotic or of a nervous disposition were cared for by the local communities who also judged them to be so. The rise of psychiatric medicine in the nineteenth century led to the development of 'mad-doctors' and specialised institutions for the treatment, or confinement, of patients.

By the turn of the twentieth century, therapeutic treatments designed to uncover the hidden dimensions of the self were being introduced. Mesmerism, hypnosis and psychoanalysis built up an understanding of a dynamic unconscious and the techniques by which it might be brought to the surface, albeit under the control of the practitioner rather than the patient.

Though Freud's 'talking cure' is probably the most well-known contemporary example, approaches such as person-centred counselling were developed as a rejection of this controlled relationship. Expressive therapies, such as art or music therapy, also provide opportunities for individuals to engage with and express their inner selves. As artist Edward Adamson wrote, 'art obliges us to communicate with the inner self, and in so doing, to engage in a dialogue with both our destructive and creative forces.'

MIND

What we call a mind, is nothing but a heap or collection of different perceptions, united together by certain relations, and suppos'd, tho, falsely, to be endow'd with a perfect simplicity and identity.

Philosopher and essayist David Hume in *A Treatise of Human Nature*, 1739–40

Flint paintings

'Skull Head'
Watercolour, Indian ink and varnish on flint
Gwyneth Rowlands, 20th century
RRa0287 / Adamson Collection Trust / L0075825 Wellcome Images

Gwyneth Rowlands's flint paintings are just some of the 5000 works collected by artist Edward Adamson (1911–96), who believed his collection could enlighten the public about the creativity and humanity of those labelled with mental illness. Rowlands spent 30 years in a mental health institution where Adamson, the first artist to be employed in a UK hospital, worked. She painted on pieces of flint discarded by local farmers in the surrounding Surrey fields, fitting intricate drawings to the jagged shapes of her found materials. Producing two to three new pieces a day, Rowlands was also allowed access to the hospital's studio at weekends.

Based on butterflies

Like many other patients, Rowlands began painting by copying. She created meticulous reproductions of stained-glass window designs and copied pictures of butterflies from books on to pebbles she found at the seaside. Swapping the pebbles for flint, Rowlands's later works are powerful expressions of her own creativity.

'Untitled' from 'Butterfly Series'
Watercolour and stone
Gwyneth Rowlands, 20th century
Adamson Collection Trust

A French writer says that all painters are more or less crazy... Whatever may be the truth of it, I imagine that here, where I don't have to care for anything, etc., I am progressing in the quality of my work. And thus, I go on with relative calmness, and do my best on my work, and don't consider myself amongst the unhappy ones.

Vincent van Gogh (1853–90) writing to his mother seven months after admitting himself to the Saint-Paul asylum in Saint-Rémy, 1889

No patients here

A pioneer of British art therapy, Edward Adamson viewed artistic expression as a healing process and allowed the people he worked with relatively free rein. He actively ignored information about their medical history, didn't teach them artistic techniques, made no suggestions about their subjects and refrained from interpreting the finished works in a psychological manner. Acting as a creative facilitator, Adamson also avoided the word 'patient', which he felt deprived a person of their individuality and labelled them as 'a specimen'.

When I visited the locked wards for the more severely disturbed, I was handed pieces of lavatory paper, on which were crude drawings, sketched out with the charred end of a matchstick. No facilities were provided for drawing.

Edward Adamson describing his first visit to the long-stay psychiatric hospital at Netherne in 1946 in *The Art of Healing*

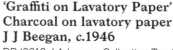

'Graffiti on Lavatory Paper'
Charcoal on lavatory paper
J J Beegan, *c.*1946
RRd0212 / Adamson Collection Trust

MIND

'Woman's Head'

'Woman's Head'
Watercolour, Indian ink and varnish on flint
Gwyneth Rowlands, 20th century
RRa0284 / Adamson Collection Trust / L0075822 Wellcome
Images

'Woman and Child'

'Woman and Child'
Watercolour, Indian ink and varnish on flint
Gwyneth Rowlands, 20th century
RRa0285 / Adamson Collection Trust / L0075824,
L0075823 Wellcome Images

'Snarling Head'

'Snarling Head'
Watercolour, Indian ink and varnish on flint
Gwyneth Rowlands, 20th century
RRa0288 / Adamson Collection Trust / L0075829 Wellcome
Images

🖉 Art from the outside

The aesthetic value of art created by mental-asylum patients was first publicly appreciated by German psychiatrist and art historian Hans Prinzhorn (1886–1933), who wrote in *Artistry of the Mentally Ill* that 'the most sovereign drawing by Rembrandt [and] the most miserable daubing by a paralytic [are both] expressions of the psyche'. Today, the term 'outsider art' encompasses works created with no audience in mind, by untrained artists on the margins of society. It is an English approximation of the French *'art brut'*, which refers to art uncontaminated by culture.

🗋 Read

Adamson E. Art as Healing. London: Coventure; 1984.
Baker B. Diary Drawings: Mental illness and me. London: Profile; 2010.
MacGregor JM. The Discovery of the Art of the Insane. New Jersey: Princeton University Press; 1993.

MIND

'Black Madonna'

'Black Madonna'
Watercolour, Indian ink and varnish on flint
Gwyneth Rowlands, 20th century
RRa0289 / Adamson Collection Trust / L0075832 Wellcome Images

'Large Face with Flowers'

'Large Face with Flowers'
Watercolour, Indian ink and varnish on flint
Gwyneth Rowlands, 20th century
RRa0290 / Adamson Collection Trust / L0075835, L0075833 Wellcome Images

'Untitled'

Metal and plastic
Shota Katsube, 2013
RRa0068 / Shota Katsube / L0075780 Wellcome Images

Japanese outsider artist Shota Katsube (b.1991) has been making armies of tiny action figures from bin-liner twist-ties since he was ten years old. His meticulous characters come complete with miniature accessories and weapons.

⌗ For no reward

Katsube's work is a prime example of what French painter and sculptor Jean Dubuffet (1901–85) named *'art brut'* in the 1940s. This 'raw' or 'crude' art was culturally unconventional and even subversive. As writer and editor John Maizels has said, it is also 'produced entirely for individual satisfaction and inner need with no regard to exhibition, fame or monetary reward'.

📖 Read

Maizels J. Raw Creation: Outsider art and beyond. London: Phaidon; 2000.
Museum het Dolhuys. Outsider Art from Japan. Haarlem: WBooks; 2012.
Peiry L. Art Brut: The origins of outsider art. Paris: Flammarion; 2006.

MIND

Bethlem Hospital almsboxes

Bethlem Hospital almsboxes
Wood, plaster and metal
*c.***1676**

RR0025.1–2 / A600163–4 Science Museum / L0076300,
L0076302 Wellcome Images

From its foundation in 1247, the priory of the Order of Bethlehem in London relied on income from property rents and charitable donations to fund its work caring for the poor, sick and elderly. Visiting friends and families were encouraged to buy food and clothes for the inmates, or make a financial contribution to the hospital's work.

In order to encourage donations, these poor boxes stood in a prominent position by the main gate of what was also known as 'Bethlem' or 'Bedlam'. By then an institution specialising in the care and protection of the 'distracted', the Bethlem boxes were said to be inscribed with the plea 'remember the poore Lunaticks'.

📖 Read

Arnold C. Bedlam: London and its mad. London: Simon & Schuster; 2009.

Barnett R. Sick City: Two thousand years of life and death in London. London: Strange Attractor; 2008.

Jay M. A The Influencing Machine: James Tilly Matthews and the air loom. London: Strange Attractor; 2012.

Peterson D. A Mad People's History of Madness. Philadelphia: University of Pittsburgh Press; 1982.

MIND

Inmates on show

More money is thought to have been put into Bethlem's poor boxes during the 1760s than in any other decade, thanks to a soaring stream of visitors. While the governors of Bethlem had encouraged the public to come and peer at the insane for many years, a trip to the hospital had become a popular spectacle, livened up by the presence of drunks, prostitutes and hawkers.

Though the opportunity to view the inmates was seen by some to be morally instructive, the practice of admitting unregulated visitors ceased in 1770, to be replaced by a ticket system. Bethlem was, by then, financially self-sufficient.

Bedlam scene from *The Rake's Progress*
Engraving
T Cook after William Hogarth, 1796
M0008974 Wellcome Images

'The Hospital of Bethlehem' at Moorfields
Coloured engraving
After Robert Hooke, *c.*1750
25614i Wellcome Library

...to my great surprise,
I found a hundred people at least,
who having paid their two-pence
a piece, were suffered unattended
to run rioting up and down the
wards, making sport and diversion
of the miserable inhabitants...
I saw the poorer wretches,
the spectators, in a loud laugh
of triumph at the ravings
they had occasioned.

A letter to *The World*, describing
a visit to Bethlem, 1753

Kaleidoscopic cats

Thanks to money raised through a public appeal, British illustrator Louis Wain (1860–1939) was transferred to a private room at Bethlem in 1925, a year after being certified insane. Already known for his humorous pictures of cats, Wain's Bethlem works include a series of striking geometric felines.

'A cat standing on its hind legs'
Gouache
Louis Wain, 1925–39
38888i Wellcome Library

Straitjackets

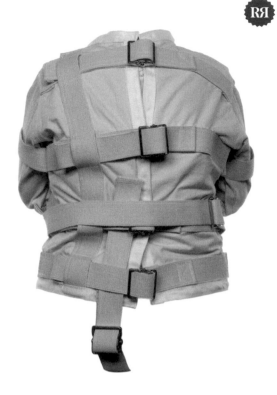

Straitjackets
Monkey Dungeon, 2014
RRc0007 / L0076120, L0076124 Wellcome Images

Despite looking like an instrument of torture, the straitjacket was originally devised as a garment that would liberate – and even cure – the mentally ill. First made by an upholsterer for Bicêtre, a hospital for insane men near Paris, the straitjacket played a key role in a revolutionary late eighteenth-century experiment, though its later uses were perhaps less well-meant.

He selected a number of individual patients – including an English sea captain who had been chained for 40 years and a priest who imagined himself Christ – and offered to remove their chains if they promised to behave. In most cases, the patient's reason was restored after (sometimes years after) they had been given their liberty.

✐ From vice to reason

Bicêtre was formerly called the *Grange aux Guex*, or the Den of Beggars. Known for harbouring vice, crime and repulsive diseases, the hospital 'cells' were portrayed by psychiatrist and biographer René Semelaigne (1855–1934) as 'frightful dens in which one would have hesitated to put the most vile of animals'. Patients were handcuffed or chained. Filled with 'indignation, despair and rage' at their cruel treatment, they would sometimes surprise their tormenters, striking them with their chains and throwing them 'expiring at their feet'.

Philippe Pinel (1745–1826), who had been sent to Bicêtre to implement reform, ignored the hospital's sanitation and administration problems and focused instead on unchaining and observing the insane.

A mentally ill patient in a straitjacket
Wood engraving
E Tritschler, 1908
20037i Wellcome Library

MIND

...the same insane who, reduced to chains for a long period of years remained in a constant state of fury, walked afterwards quietly with a simple straightjacket and talked to everyone...

Philippe Pinel, quoted by Louis H Cohen in 'The Experiment at Bicêtre: 1793', *Yale Journal of Biology and Medicine*, 1932

Sometimes I continu'd in the Bed all the Day: Sometimes they put Bolts upon my Hands and Fetters on my Feet, when I prov'd violent and unruly (which I often did); for I would often strive and fight... to get away from them, and so to free my self from that Place, which thought to have been Hell...

Presbyterian minister George Trosse describing his experience in a 'Physician's House' in *The Life of the Reverend Mr George Trosse*, 1714

The memory jacket

In the Prinzhorn Collection at the psychiatric hospital of the University of Heidelberg is a linen jacket sewn and worn by a seamstress, Agnes Richter, who was an inmate in a Dresden asylum in the late nineteenth century. The entire garment is embroidered with texts – some legible, others indecipherable – and may have functioned as a kind of diary, as the label suggests: 'Memories of her life in the seams of every piece of washing and clothing'.

Political caricature featuring a straitjacket
Etching
Thomas Rowlandson, 1784
12171i Wellcome Library

This satirical cartoon shows Bedlam physician Dr Monro referring to the sad case of politician Charles James Fox (1749–1806): 'As I have not the least hope of his recovery, let him be remov'd amongst the incurable's', a comment on the fall of the short-lived coalition Fox had formed with his former adversary.

Read

Connolly J. The Treatment of the Insane Without Mechanical Restraints. Cambridge: Cambridge University Press; 2014.

Foucault M. History of Madness. Abingdon: Routledge; 2006.

Moncrieff J. The Bitterest Pills: The troubling story of antipsychotic drugs. Basingstoke: Palgrave; 2013.

Valenstein ES. Blaming the Brain: The truth about drugs and mental health. New York: Free Press; 1998.

La camisole chimique

Like the straitjacket before it, chlorpromazine, the first antipsychotic drug to become an established treatment, was hailed by many as an effective way of liberating psychiatric patients from restraints and locked wards. Synthesised in 1950 at Rhône-Poulenc in France, the drug induced 'artificial hibernation' when first tested at the Val-de-Grâce military hospital in Paris. Follow-up trials by psychiatrists Jean Delay and Pierre Denker indicated chlorpromazine could reduce excitation and agitation in manic patients, who tended to stay still and silent, showing a detached indifference to the world around them.

Within 13 years, around 10 000 chlorpromazine-related research articles had been produced; by 1970, Smith Kline & French's sales of the drug (under the trade name Thorazine) totalled over $116 million. By this time, critics of the drug were calling it the *'camisole chimique'*, or chemical straitjacket. The similarities may be strong, but forcing someone to take a drug, which enters the patient's body and causes physical or mental changes, could be viewed as a much greater violation of an individual's autonomy than putting them in a straitjacket.

MIND

'Mesmeric Therapy'

'Mesmeric Therapy'
Oil on canvas
French school, 1778–84
RRa0006 / 44754i Wellcome Library

A fashionable spectacle in the salons of eighteenth-century Paris, mesmerism induced a trance state designed to restore harmony between the individual and the universe. Named, originally pejoratively, after German physician Franz Anton Mesmer (seen holding a wand at the rear right of this crowd), mesmerism came to encompass a range of techniques that acquired control over the individual – in both body and mind.

Read

Crabtree A. From Mesmer to Freud: Magnetic sleep and the roots of psychological hearing. New Haven: Yale University Press; 2012.

Winter A. Mesmerized: Powers of mind in Victorian Britain. Chicago: Chicago University Press; 1998.

Animal magnetism

Born on the shores of Lake Constance, Franz Mesmer (1734–1815) originally trained to be a priest, but later studied medicine. In his MD thesis, he studied the influence of the Sun and the Moon on the human body. Mesmer believed in a magnetic force called 'animal magnetism', which he sought to transmit to patients by making long, sweeping movements over their skin.

Thin bilious persons of a sanguine constitution whose nervous system is irritable, are commonly those on whom, it seems to me, Animal Magnetics have the greatest power.

M Caullet de Veaumore in *Mesmer's Aphorisms and Instructions*, 1785

The magnetic bathtub

Mesmer's 'baquet', a circular tub with a cover, contained bottles of magnetised water connected to patients by metal rods. It was housed in a darkened room where soft music played and Mesmer intoned healing thoughts. Patients who failed to gain access to the baquet weren't entirely overlooked; they might be offered a magnetised tree instead.

'Le Baquet de Mesmer'
Engraving
M0006352 Wellcome Images

A somnambulist and a tree
From *Memoires pour Servir a l'Histoire*
et a l'Etablissement du Magnetisme Animal
A M J Chastenet, 1820
b10707803 Wellcome Library

Mesmerism on trial

In 1784, King Louis XVI (1754–93) set up a Royal Commission, which included Benjamin Franklin, Joseph Guillotin and Antoine Lavoisier, to investigate animal magnetism. The commission failed to prove its existence and Mesmer was forced to retire, though his technique lived on without him. The final report of the commission stated:

> 'The Commissioners have found that…this fluid had no action, either on the Commissioners or on the patients subjected to it… They have come to the following unanimous conclusion about the existence and utility of animal magnetism. There is nothing to prove the existence of the magnetic fluid; that this fluid, since it is non-existent, can have no salubrious influence…'

He mesmerised you; that's what it is – mesmerism!... They get you into their power, and just make you do any blessed thing they please – lie, murder, steal – anything! And kill yourself into the bargain when they've done with you! It's just too terrible to think of!

From George du Maurier's *Trilby*, 1894

Nineteenth-century witchcraft

The potential of mesmerism (and its successor, hypnotism) to control and manipulate minds with malign intent caused considerable anxiety among sceptics. American author Nathaniel Hawthorne (1804–64) entreated his wife to eschew such 'magnetic miracles', fearing the loss of the self. In his 1851 novel *The House of the Seven Gables*, Hawthorne correlates mesmerism with witchcraft and depicts it as an abuse of power that removes the victim's autonomy and invades their very soul.

George du Maurier's (1834–96) runaway bestseller *Trilby* featured a domineering hypnotist whose name has since become synonymous with a controlling individual operating for evil intent. He was, of course, Svengali.

MIND

Theatrical replica of Sigmund Freud's couch

> I cannot put up
> with being stared at
> by other people
> for eight hours a day
> (or more).
>
> Sigmund Freud in *On Beginning the Treatment*, 1913

Theatrical replica of Sigmund Freud's couch
Mixed materials
Hampstead Theatre, 2013
RRc0003 / L0075863 Wellcome Images

Made to star in a 2013 production of Terry Johnson's play *Hysteria*, this couch is a copy of the Victorian chaise longue that still stands in what was Sigmund Freud's (1856–1939) Hampstead study. The 'analytical couch' may have become a symbol of psychoanalysis, but it was actually a hangover from the psychiatrist's early use of hypnosis. Although it's not clear whether Freud always used this reclining approach, he did advise that a patient who resisted an invitation to lie on the couch should be refused treatment.

Avoiding eye contact

Freud, who sat out of sight at the head of the couch, recommended its use for two reasons. Firstly, it meant his patients were unable to scrutinise him. Secondly, if freed from the conversational conventions associated with eye-to-eye contact, patients would, he hoped, be more likely to engage in the free associations that disclosed their unconscious thoughts. This lack of eye contact could, of course, be achieved by other means, such as placing the chairs of analyst and patient at right angles, or positioning them a substantial distance apart.

A charmed relic

Novelist and historian Marina Warner (b.1946) describes Freud's couch as a charmed relic. Saturated with historic memories, the couch is, says Warner, 'a thing changed and affected by its uses'.

Hysteria on stage

First staged by director Phyllida Lloyd at London's Royal Court Theatre in 1993, Terry Johnson's *Hysteria* is both sinister and absurd. Set in Freud's study in 1938, the play traps the psychoanalyst in a nightmarish cycle of covering, uncovering, repressing and exposing knowledge.

MIND

Hypnotic influences

Jean-Martin Charcot demonstrating hysteria in a patient at the Salpêtrière, Paris
Etching
A Lurat, 1888 after
Pierre A A Brouillet, 1887
545647i Wellcome Library

Freud hung a print of this scene above the couch in his London study, a symbol of the impact the four months he spent with Jean-Martin Charcot in 1885–86 had on him. Charcot (1825–93) used hypnosis to treat women suffering from hysteria (see p. 153), the same condition with which the famed patient Anna O had been diagnosed.

In Freud's 1895 book *Studies on Hysteria*, written with his mentor – and Anna O's physician – Josef Breuer (1842–1925), Freud concluded that hysteria was rooted in painful buried memories. Though Freud later abandoned hypnosis, which he declared a 'temperamental and, one might almost say, a mystical ally', his 'talking cure' focused on excavating these hidden experiences.

Sleepwalking into authoritarianism

Fritz Lang's 1922 film *Dr Mabuse: The Gambler* features a sinister criminal mastermind who relies on hypnosis to control and seduce everyone he meets. It has been argued that Lang's use of hypnotism was an allegory for Germany's troubled political and social milieu. At the time, the nation was arguably sleepwalking into authoritarianism and, later, totalitarianism.

Describing the unseen

Free association was an overriding rule of Freud's approach. In his 1913 essay *On Beginning the Treatment*, Freud recommended introducing the concept to a patient by asking them to act like a traveller on a train who describes everything he sees out the window to other passengers, who cannot see what he does.

If imagining trains and lying on a couch doesn't get the free association going, there are other options. Ink-blot tests and word-association activities have both been used to try to gain a sense of what is lurking in the unconscious. Freud was also a proponent of dream interpretation, describing it as 'the royal road to a knowledge of the unconscious activities of the mind'.

This procedure was one of clearing away the pathogenic psychical material layer by layer, and we liked to compare it with the technique of excavating a buried city.

From the case study of Elisabeth von R in Breuer and Freud's *Studies on Hysteria*, 1895

Read

Freud S: An Introduction to Psychoanalysis. Hertfordshire: Wordsworth Classics of World Literature; 2012.

Grosz S. The Examined Life: How we lose and find ourselves. London: Vintage; 2014.

Johnson T. Hysteria. London: Bloomsbury; 2013.

Lohsher B, Lewton PM. Unorthodox Freud: The view from the couch. New York: Guildford Press; 1996.

Malcolm J. Psychoanalysis: The impossible profession. Cambridge: Granta; 2012.

Shepphard R. Explorer of the Mind: The illustrated biography of Sigmund Freud. London: André Deutsch; 2012.

MIND

'Sewing Body'

RR

I had developed some sort of obsession that all my daily objects were becoming rapidly obsolete and that they were going to disappear soon. At a time when we are experiencing machines 'memorising' for us, we can see how our own memory is 'reinventing' its process.

Artist Alice Anderson

'Sewing Body'
Copper wire and mixed materials
Alice Anderson, 2012
RRa0283 / L0075819 Wellcome Images

Underneath the tightly wound copper wire of 'Sewing Body' lies a needlework figure once used by filmmaker and artist Alice Anderson's (b.1972) grandmother. As with the video camera she first weaved in copper, and the other objects and architectural features she later bound, Anderson has committed never to unwind the work, or to buy replacements.

Like mummified bodies protected from decay, these items are saved from being forgotten. Questioning the concept of memory and our relationships with objects, Anderson's process fundamentally alters the wound object and suggests alternative ways of remembering. She herself remembers these works not from the resulting sculptures but from the performances that created them.

Read

Aboujaoude E. Compulsive Acts: A psychiatrist's tales of ritual and obsession. Berkeley: University of California Press; 2008.
Deleuze G. Difference and Repetition. London: Continuum; 2001.

Hysterical sewing

When needlework became a gendered activity in the eighteenth and nineteenth centuries, the pastime taught girls not just how to sew, but how to conform to the norms of femininity: sitting quietly and following established patterns. Freud thought girls and young women with lively imaginations were numbed by the monotony of long hours of sewing, an activity that might also provide ample opportunity for the daydreams he believed formed the basis of hysteria.

Winding around the Freud Museum

In 2011, Anderson wound twisted ropes of red fibre material around the former home of Sigmund Freud (now the Freud Museum).

MIND

'Housebound'
Alice Anderson, 2011
Alice Anderson

📎 Weaving webs

Spiders and web
From *Commentarii in Libros Sex Pedacii*
Dioscorides Anazarbei de Materia Medica
Pietra Andreci Mattioli
M0012576 Wellcome Images

In Roman poet Ovid's (43 BCE–*c.*18 CE) *Metamorphoses*, when the goddess Minerva discovers that Arachne's fame as a worker in wool has equalled her own, she tears up Arachne's tapestry and turns her into a spider.

Arachne's hair dropped off;
her nose and ears vanished, and
her head was shrunken; her whole
body was contracted. From her
side thin fingers dangled for legs,
and the rest became her belly.

From Ovid's *Metamorphoses*

📎 De-limbing dad

Louise Bourgeois (1911–2010) is another artist renowned for using her art as a repository and interrogator of her own memories. As a child, Bourgeois moulded her 'first sculptural solution', a figure of her father, out of white bread, before slowly and ritualistically cutting off the arms and legs with a knife. Bourgeois's late series of fabric sculptures, fashioned with needle and thread, recalls her mother's tapestry-repair workshop.

MIND

Clarke-style electromagnetic machine

...[electrotherapy is] another instance of those chimerical fancies of the day, which are perpetually disgracing our profession, and bringing it into contempt with the public; that, like mesmerism, it will meet with a similar fate...

William Beven
in the *London Medical Gazette*, 1842

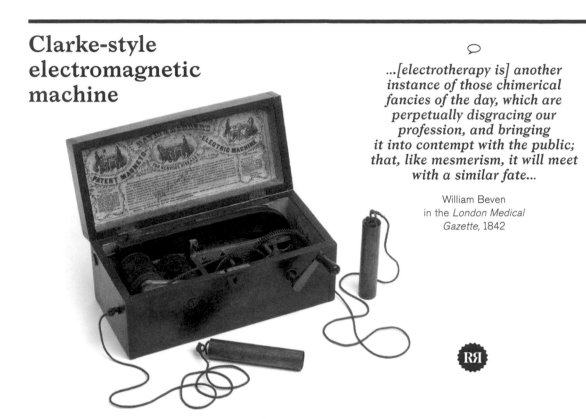

Clarke-style electromagnetic machine
Wood and metal
W H Burnap, 1854–60
RRa0116 / A116662 Science Museum / L0076060
Wellcome Images

Sparked by the advent in 1754 of the Leyden jar – a device that stored and released electrical charges on demand – electrotherapy became an accepted medical technique. From the end of the nineteenth century until World War I, it was the preferred treatment for many mental illnesses. The instructions accompanying this electromagnetic machine suggest its use for hysteria, a condition that has been variously attributed to both physical and mental causes.

Electric conversation

Responses to the uses of electricity on the human body have ranged from horror to humour. Published in 1818, Mary Shelley's *Frankenstein* paints a dark and terrifying picture of a monstrous creature brought to life by electricity only to cause chaos and misery. In 1845, Edgar Allen Poe published his satirically comic short story, *Some Words with a Mummy*, in which a group of educated men reanimate an Egyptian mummy with electricity and converse with him on the superiority of their modern culture – only to realise that, in fact, their knowledge hardly surpasses the ancient Egyptians' at all, save for the invention of the cough drop.

Primitive cures

In his 1747 book *Primitive Remedies*, the founder of the Methodist Church, John Wesley (1703–91), listed almost 300 medical conditions that could be prevented or healed by electricity. Some of his recommended treatments included administering up to a hundred shocks.

'Mysteria'

Despite his renown as a specialist in 'the female condition', Philadelphia neurologist Silas Weir Mitchell (1829–1914) was so confounded by the trances, fits, choking and hair-tearing of his hysterical patients that he sometimes called the condition 'Mysteria'. His 'rest cure' involved isolating the patient from their friends and family for six to eight weeks, enforced bed rest and a high-fat diet.

MIND

The wandering womb

The word 'hysteria' comes from the Greek *hysterikos*, meaning 'of the womb', an organ the ancient Greeks believed travelled around the body. The wandering womb was blamed for a multitude of symptoms. For instance, if it moved upwards, the uterus might cause shortness of breath, chest pains or choking.

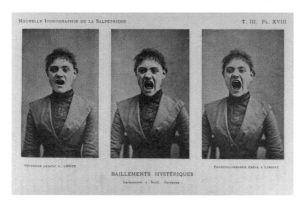

A hysterical woman yawning
Photograph
Albert Londe, *c*.1890
L0034940 Wellcome Images

Driven mad by rest

American author Charlotte Perkins Gilman's (1860–1935) short story *The Yellow Wallpaper* tells the chilling first-person tale of a young woman whose physician husband considers her to have 'a slight hysterical tendency'. Prescribed 'phosphates or phosphites – whichever it is, and tonics and journeys, and air and exercise' and 'absolutely forbidden to "work"', when confined to a room for three months she gradually becomes insane.

Gilman herself suffered from depression. After consulting Silas Weir Mitchell, she was prescribed a rest cure but gave it up when her depression worsened.

Personally, I believe that congenial work, with excitement and change, would do me good. But what is one to do? I did write for a while in spite of them; but it does exhaust me a good deal – having to be so sly about it, or else meet with heavy opposition.

From Charlotte Perkins Gilman's *The Yellow Wallpaper*, 1892

Not just for women

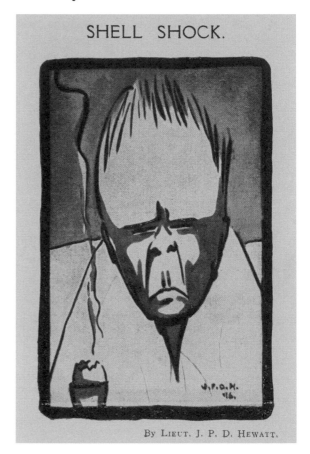

'Shell Shock'
From *The Fourth* magazine, 1917
J P D Hewatt
L0046100 Wellcome Images

In the twentieth century, hysteria – previously thought to be a physical illness – was commonly accepted as an affliction of the mind expressed through physical symptoms. The shell shock suffered by World War I soldiers was initially categorised as a neurological disorder, but later described as male hysteria.

Read

Morus IW. Shocking Bodies: Life, death & electricity in Victorian England. Stroud: The History Press; 2011.

Scull A. Hysteria: The disturbing history. Oxford: Oxford University Press; 2012.

MIND

Trephination set

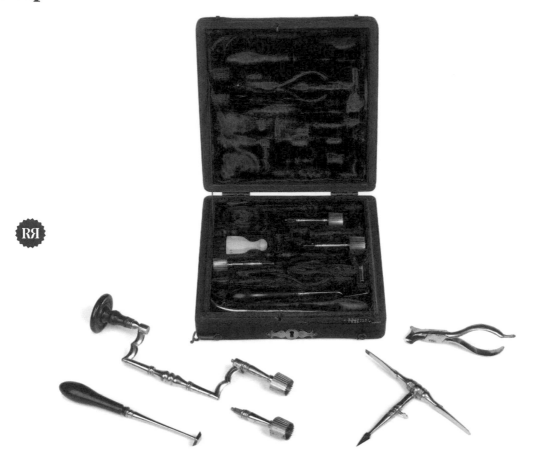

MIND

Trephination set
Wood, fish skin, velvet and brass
1893–1930
RRa0115 / A616092 Science Museum / L0076319
Wellcome Images

Dating back to at least Neolithic times, trepanation (or trephination) is the oldest known surgical procedure. Trepanation operations have been conducted for a wide range of purposes, including the relief of depressions or fractures of the skull and the release of demons or humours thought to cause headaches or epilepsy. Their popularity has waxed and waned through the centuries.

This instrument set contains drills with cylindrical blades, rugines to remove connective tissue from bones, lenticulars to depress brain matter and a brush to remove fine fragments of bone.

RIGHT: **Trephination operation**
From *A Compleat Discourse of Wounds*
John Browne, 1678
b12221260 Wellcome Library

Just for the French?

In the seventeenth century, English physician Thomas Willis made his opinions about trepanation clear when surgeon William Harvey suggested he use the method on a patient suffering from migraine. Willis considered it a dangerous operation that was, at the time, rarely performed except by the French. 'Truly', he wrote, 'it does not appear to me what certainty we may expect from the Scull being opened where it pains.'

*I think the opening
of the skull will profit nothing.*

English physician Thomas Willis (1621-75)

To ensnare

Dr Johnson's dictionary defines the verb 'trepan' as both the process of cutting with a surgeon's instrument and to catch or ensnare. In Robert Louis Stevenson's 1886 novel *Kidnapped*, the protagonist recounts his fate as, '…I was trepanned on board the brig, cruelly struck down, thrown below, and knew no more of anything till we were far at sea'.

Opening the mind

In 1970, artist Amanda Feilding (b.1943) trepanned herself after observing that friends who had under-gone the procedure exhibited a 'lessening of the neurotic behaviour that we all have' or no longer experienced headaches. Feilding spent four years trying unsuccessfully to persuade a doctor to trepan her before, after much careful preparation, she per-formed the operation herself, using local anaesthetic and an electric drill. At the time, she described the immediate result as 'feeling like the tide coming in… of rising, slowly and gently, to levels that felt good.' Her dreams also became much less anxious.

In 1979 and 1983, Feilding stood for Parliament in her local Chelsea constituency, with the manifesto 'Trepanation for the National Health'. She is now director of The Beckley Foundation, a trust that conducts research into consciousness and the functioning of the brain.

The 'Hat On–Hat Off' man

In 1958, Edward Margetts (1920–2004), the Canadian psychiatrist in charge of Nairobi's Mathari Mental Hospital, reported on a Kenyan trepanation he described as 'the most spectacular curiosity that one would ever hope to see'. When wearing his hat, 50-year-old Nyachoti from the Kisii district in Kenya looked entirely unobtrusive. When he took his hat off, the top of Nyachoti's head appeared missing, thanks to a 30-square-inch hole in his skull, a result of multiple trepanations conducted to relieve chronic headaches. Margetts nicknamed the case, and Nyachoti himself, 'Hat On–Hat Off'.

Nyachoti, also known as 'Hat On–Hat Off'
Photograph
Edward Margetts, 1958
Dr Sloan Mahone, University of Oxford

Read

Gross CG. A Hole in the Head: More tales in the history of neuroscience. Cambridge: MIT Press; 2009.
Kwint M, Wingate R. Brains: The mind as matter. London: Profile Books; 2012.

MIND

Stitched drawings of elderly patients
Georgie Meadows, 2011

Lives

Though the term 'biography' (meaning 'depiction of life') was not coined until the late seventeenth century, people have been making and sharing stories and portraits of themselves, or others, for millennia. Images of stick-like humans feature in Palaeolithic cave paintings; many cultures commemorate individuals through poems, songs and spoken sagas; and portraits of a kind feature on Egyptian sarcophagi, Greek busts and early coins from Asia Minor. In each case – as it would be for the painted or photographic portraits, 'authorised' or 'unauthorised' biographies, journals, diaries, tweets or selfies that followed – the 'truth' they represent is uncertain.

The purpose of most early biographies was, like a naturalistic portrait, to commemorate a venerable subject and chronicle their journey through life. It wasn't until James Boswell's warts-and-all portrayal of Samuel Johnson that revealing the intimate truth became the norm. The intimate truth of patients' selves, however, has not always been as exposed as the lives of the doctors who treat them; medical case histories, after all, present a life story from a very specific perspective.

When someone records or compiles their own story, a new kind of truth emerges. Like the narrative that unfolds from Henry Wellcome's extensive collection, or the shared insights in Montaigne's *Essais*, the value in diaries or self-portraits comes not from their presentation of documentary evidence but from what they reveal about the creator's character, emotions and self-image. Even a biased or twisted representation communicates something about the individual's inner self. Autobiographies present yet another tale, one that might challenge other accounts of the author, or be censored or manipulated by its subject.

The most brilliant exploits often tell us nothing of the virtues and vices of the men who performed them...a chance remark or a joke may reveal far more of a man's character than the mere feat of winning battles in which thousands fall... it is my task to dwell upon those actions which illuminate the workings of the soul, and by this means to create a portrait of each man's life.

Plutarch in *The Life of Alexander*, 1st century CE

Stitched drawings of elderly patients

Stitched drawing
Glass and textile
Georgie Meadows, 2011
RRa0053 / L0075749 Wellcome Images

Georgie Meadows's stitched drawings of elderly patients, squeezed and preserved in jars like sterile museum specimens, question how individual experiences of ageing and dementia are commonly interpreted.

LIVES

At first I showed the stitched work pinned on the wall or hung in acrylic boxes. However, when I experimented with putting them into jars in a row on a shelf, everything changed. These people no longer had a story, they no longer had any privacy, they were restricted, they had no autonomy, they were safely preserved on a shelf, going nowhere. So the work in jars poses a question: is this what we are doing to the elderly, to the infirm?

Artist Georgie Meadows describing
her stitched portraits

📎 New ways of looking

Having worked as an occupational therapist for many years, Meadows used textile works to illustrate the unique individuality and experiences of her patients. By encouraging empathy, Meadows hopes to challenge misleading assumptions and prompt imaginative thinking around care practices. Her work also celebrates the courage of older people as they face daily mental and physical struggles and adapt to diminished roles within society.

Stitched drawing
Glass and textile
Georgie Meadows, 2011
RRa0054 / L0075750 Wellcome Images

Stitched drawing
Glass and textile
Georgie Meadows, 2011
RRa0056 / L0075752 Wellcome Images

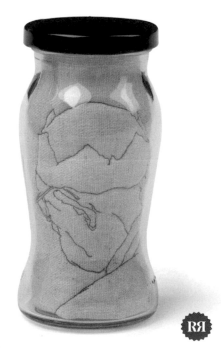

Stitched drawing
Glass and textile
Georgie Meadows, 2011
RRa0055 / L0075751 Wellcome Images

LIVES

Stitched drawing
Glass and textile
Georgie Meadows, 2011
RRa0057 / L0075753 Wellcome Images

Stitched drawing
Glass and textile
Georgie Meadows, 2011
RRa0060 / L0075756 Wellcome Images

Stitched drawing
Glass and textile
Georgie Meadows, 2011
RRa0058 / L0075754 Wellcome Images

Stitched drawing
Glass and textile
Georgie Meadows, 2011
RRa0061 / L0075757 Wellcome Images

Stitched drawing
Glass and textile
Georgie Meadows, 2011
RRa0062 / L0075758 Wellcome Images

Stitched drawing
Glass and textile
Georgie Meadows, 2011
RRa0059 / L0075755 Wellcome Images

*Show me a man who longs to live
beyond his time who turns his
back on a decent length of life,
I'll show the world a man who
clings to folly.
For the long, looming days lay up
a thousand things closer to pain
than pleasure, and the pleasures
disappear...*

From *Oedipus Coloneus* by Sophocles,
5th century BCE

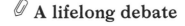

𝒪 A lifelong debate

In scenes ranging from the Garden of Eden to the far future, George Bernard Shaw's 1921 play *Back to Methuselah* argues in favour of longer human lifespans. Living longer, Shaw suggests, would encourage governments that consider the long-term factors necessary to perfect human existence.

Czech writer Karel Čapek argued the reverse. In his 1925 play *The Makropoulos Secret*, his aged heroine consumes an elixir for eternal life and lives to be more than 300 years old. After operating under a series of false identities, to avoid arousing suspicion, she feels she has tried all life has to offer and grows cynical. At last, she realises that death is necessary if life is to have meaning.

Stitched drawing
Glass and textile
Georgie Meadows, 2011
RRa0063 / L0075759 Wellcome Images

Self-portraits by an artist with Alzheimer's disease

'Figure in Studio with Mug'
Giclee print
William Utermohlen, 1995
RRa0077 / William Utermohlen

When 61-year-old American artist William Utermohlen (1933–2007) was diagnosed with Alzheimer's disease in 1995, he embarked on a series of self-portraits to help understand what was happening to his mind. The results illustrate the development of his condition over an eight-year period, providing a unique artistic and medical record of life with dementia.

Utermohlen's paintings are influenced by his deteriorating motor control, changes in his spatial perception and the artist's response to his condition. Over time, Utermohlen was forced to swap oil paints for easier-to-use pencils, and his ability to accurately represent facial features declined. In later drawings, the features blur together, appear strangely disjointed or even disappear entirely.

Painting, said Utermohlen, 'is always about how you feel'. These works illustrate his own contorted limbs, with compositions that reflect an increasingly fragmented, claustrophobic and silent world.

'In the Studio (Self-Portrait)'

'In the Studio (Self-Portrait)'
Giclee print
William Utermohlen, 1996
RRa0076 / William Utermohlen

'Twisted Figure in Chair'

'Twisted Figure in Chair'
Giclee print
William Utermohlen, 1996
RRa0078 / William Utermohlen

LIVES

'Self-Portrait (with Saw)'

'Self-Portrait (with Saw)'
Giclee print
William Utermohlen, 1997
RRa0074 / William Utermohlen

Utermohlen began this self-portrait on the day he willed his brain to science. The striking saw suggests the act of dissection.

'Head 1'

'Head 1'
Giclee print
William Utermohlen, 2000
RRa0075 / William Utermohlen

This contorted, eyeless portrait is the last work Utermohlen produced before his death in 2007.

A blissful lapse

The award-winning South Korean film *Poetry* (2010) offers a striking alternative to familiar Hollywood depictions of dementia. Rather than focusing on the difficult choices and narrative arc of a caregiver coming to terms with a traumatic end-of-life scenario, *Poetry* explores how Alzheimer's affects language and its relationship to memory.

After hearing her diagnosis described in the context of forgetting words, the central character starts to pursue a childhood ambition to write poetry. Her efforts generate new ways of commemorating the past, and drive her to a moment of memory loss interpreted as a blissful lapse rather than a loss of self. Memory, the film suggests, is a mixed blessing.

A dementia page-turner

Alice LaPlante's thriller about a woman with Alzheimer's who is accused of murdering her best friend won the Wellcome Book Prize in 2011. Judge Roger Highfield described *Turn of Mind* as 'a page-turner about dementia, which I never thought possible'.

Read

LaPlante A. Turn of Mind. London: Vintage; 2012.
Baker B. Diary Drawings: Mental illness and me. London: Profile Books; 2010.
Cumming L. A Face to the World: On self-portraits. London: HarperPress; 2009.
Woodall J. Portraiture: Facing the subject. Manchester: Manchester University Press; 1997.

Documenting the changing self

Many artists make their own changing and changeable bodies an important theme of their work. Rembrandt (1606–69) painted self-portraits throughout his life, from raffish youth to unsentimentally depicted old age, even showing what may be the result of a botched ear piercing. American artist Cindy Sherman (b.1954) has made a life's work out of photographing herself in clothes and settings of various disturbing personae. And Sir Antony Gormley (b.1950) uses the dimensions of his own body as parameters that determine the forms of his sculptures, which range from the clearly figurative to almost geometric abstraction.

LIVES

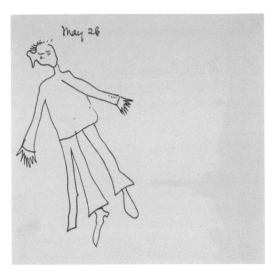

Self-portrait
Pen and ink on paper
Peter Medawar, 1970
L0073429 Wellcome Images

Immunologist Peter Medawar drew this self-portrait
in a respite home after suffering a stroke the year
before.

Identity
Digital artwork
Shelley James, 2005
B0006145 Wellcome Images

Shelley James's work questions the definition of self
and the connection between inner experience and
outer appearance.

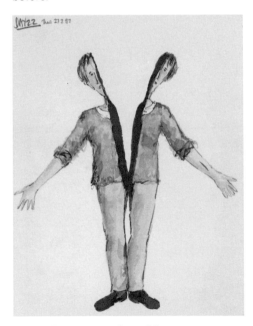

Diary Drawings: Day 22
Bobby Baker
1997–2008
B0007866 Wellcome Images

Over 11 years, performance artist Bobby Baker drew
a series of artworks while being treated for border-
line personality disorder (a label Baker describes as
'flawed') in day hospitals and acute psychiatric wards.
Initially kept to herself, the drawings gradually became a tool to help Baker communicate her complex
thoughts and emotions.

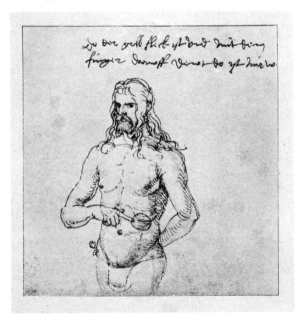

Self-portrait
Albrecht Dürer, 1519
L0006082 Wellcome Images

The inscription on this self-portrait of German artist
Albrecht Dürer (1471–1528) translates as 'Where the
yellow spot is and where I am pointing with my finger,
that is where it hurts.'

'Patient 19'

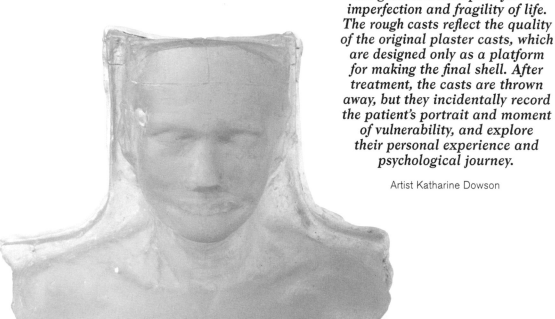

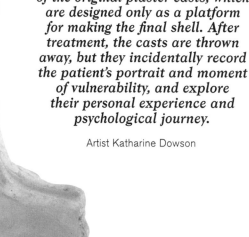

The glass is a metaphor for the imperfection and fragility of life. The rough casts reflect the quality of the original plaster casts, which are designed only as a platform for making the final shell. After treatment, the casts are thrown away, but they incidentally record the patient's portrait and moment of vulnerability, and explore their personal experience and psychological journey.

Artist Katharine Dowson

'Patient 19'
Gaffer glass
Katharine Dowson, 2012
RRa0065 / L0075766 Wellcome Images

Part of a series entitled 'Silent Stories', Katharine Dowson's glass sculpture is made from the discarded plaster cast of the face of a cancer patient. These casts are a by-product in the fabrication of individual Perspex or plastic masks, which are required to hold patients' heads in precise positions while receiving radiotherapy.

Reminiscent of a heroic classical bust, 'Patient 19' records a moment of personal vulnerability during a complex emotional journey. A hospital technician who makes the plaster casts describes the job as an intimate process, during which the need to put anxious patients at ease is as important as the technical mould-making.

Read

Mukherjee S. The Emperor of All Maladies: A biography of cancer. London: Fourth Estate; 2011.

A burdensome mask?

The study and treatment of tumours – oncology – takes its name from the Greek word *onkos*, meaning mass, load or burden. In Greek theatre, the *onkos* is a cone-shaped extension added to a tragic mask to present a larger-than-life image.

The glass delusion

Charles VI of France (1368–1422) is said to have believed he was made of glass, and had iron ribs sewn into his clothes for fear of his body shattering. From the seventeenth to the nineteenth century, glass or pottery delusions were standard psychiatric diagnoses. Patients exhibited an obsessive fear of breaking into pieces, and avoided being pushed or touched. In Miguel Cervantes's 1613 novella *El Licenciado Vidriera* (*The Glass Graduate*), a young man who believes he is made of glass walks down the centre of streets, sleeps in the open air and travels packed in straw.

LIVES

Dr Barnardo's writing desk

Dr Barnardo's writing desk
Mahogany, leather
Late 19th century
RRc0002 / L0075865 Wellcome Images

Dublin-born Thomas John Barnardo (1845–1905) was originally destined for the China Inland Mission but headed first to London. He enrolled to study medicine at the London Hospital in Whitechapel in 1866, soon after cholera had swept through the poverty-stricken East End. Within a year, he had set up a 'ragged school' in the area, providing education, shelter and food for local children. This was soon followed by a home for destitute boys, where Barnardo promised no child would be refused admission. By the time of his death, Barnardo's charity was running almost a hundred homes, caring for over 8500 children.

Thomas Barnardo at his desk
Barnardo's

✏ Family heirlooms

In 1901, Barnardo became Henry Wellcome's father-in-law, when 47-year-old Wellcome married Syrie Barnardo, just 21. The marriage lasted only nine years

and details of the relationship are sparse; acting rather out of character for such a highly acquisitive collector, Wellcome destroyed almost every letter and document relating to their time together.

Sir Henry Wellcome
and Gwendoline Syrie Wellcome
Photograph
Lafayette Ltd.
14327i Wellcome Library

✏ A miserable image

Acutely aware of his own image, Barnardo wrote to the *East London Observer* in 1877 to complain about how he was being portrayed: 'I understand that a very imperfect proof of a miserable photograph of myself, condemned when first taken, and never since circulated, has been recently exposed for sale in certain East End shops. The professed likeness is a wretched caricature… I am compelled to authorise the publication of a carte-de-visite which shall faithfully depict my physiognomy…'

✏ Barnardo's memorial

When Barnardo died in 1905, it was Henry Wellcome who organised and paid for his funeral, a major undertaking almost reaching the scale of a state occasion. Barnardo's body lay in state in Limehouse for four days before being processed through East End streets densely packed with hushed mourners; the horse-drawn carriage was followed by 1500 boys from Barnardo Homes. The funeral also involved transporting the coffin by underground train – one of only two times this has happened in the Tube's 150-year history.

LIVES

📎 'Artistic fictions'

Barnardo's innovative marketing efforts led him to appear in court in 1876, accused of deception. To advertise the success of his work and campaign for donations, Barnardo produced powerful 'before' and 'after' photographs of the boys whose lives and circumstances he worked to improve. Minister George Reynolds called one of these images an 'artistic fiction' and claimed '[Barnardo] tears their clothes, so as to make them appear worse than they really are'.

Based on the testimony of children and parents, the court agreed Barnardo had created 'fictitious representations of destitution' in order to make money. In his defence, Barnardo explained that his photographs were never intended to be realistic portraits of specific individuals. Like a painting or a novel, they were, instead, 'representative' images illustrating the deep truth of the children with whom he typically worked.

BELOW: **Children (captioned as 'raw material') outside a Barnardo home Photograph Stepney Causeway Studio**
L0000901 Wellcome Images

It is not by the direct method of a scrupulous narration that the explorer of the past can hope to depict that singular epoch. If he is wise, he will adopt a subtler strategy. He will attack his subject in unexpected places; he will fall upon the flank, or the rear; he will shoot a sudden, revealing searchlight into obscure recesses, hitherto undivined. He will row out over that great ocean of material, and lower down into it, here and there, a little bucket, which will bring up to the light of day some characteristic specimen, from those far depths, to be examined with a careful curiosity.

Lytton Strachey in the preface to *Eminent Victorians*, 1918

📄 Read

Wagner G. Barnardo. London: Weidenfeld & Nicolson; 1979.

📎 Biased lives

The enduring reputation of many Renaissance artists rests on the versions of their lives brought to us by one man, Giorgio Vasari (1511–74). Vasari's *Lives of the Artists* (1550) is rich with stories and anecdotes, not all of them factual. Famously, the book also

LIVES

exhibits a bias towards fellow Florentine artists at the expense of those from other regions of Italy.

Many subjects of biographies censor or control how their life stories are told: novelist Henry James burned many of his papers and letters; Thomas Hardy penned his own biography (but attributed it to his wife); and *The Autobiography of Alice B Toklas* is, in fact, authored by her partner Gertrude Stein.

The life of 'this creature'

The first autobiography in English is often ascribed to Margery Kempe of King's Lynn in Norfolk. She wrote of her life in 1438. Or, rather, because she was illiterate, she dictated it to a scribe in the third person, often referring to herself as 'this creature'.

The life Kempe documents was extraordinarily full for the time. She bore 14 children, travelled several times on pilgrimage – reaching Jerusalem and Santiago de Compostela – and was known as a mystic. Kempe recounts the difficulties her religious visions caused with the ecclesiastical and civil authorities, who viewed her as a threat to community order.

Tests and tastes of life

Describing his work as 'the only book in the world of its kind, a book with a wild eccentric plan', Michel Eyquem de Montaigne (1533–92) wrote not of his deeds or achievements, nor did he report on historical events. Instead, over a period of 20 years, Montaigne wrote over 100 experimental, stand-alone pieces, with titles such as 'How our mind hinders itself', 'Of the custom of wearing clothes', 'Of solitude' and 'Of the vanity of words'.

Michel de Montaigne
Photograph after a print
E Desmaisons
14025i Wellcome Library

For such a new genre, Montaigne needed a new descriptive term. He chose the word in his native French that meant to try, test or taste something: *essai*.

Warts and all

Samuel Johnson
From *The Life of Samuel Johnson*,
Eighth Edition, 1816
b12824045 Wellcome Library

James Boswell's *The Life of Samuel Johnson* (1791) was a revolutionary type of biography. Not content with simply memorialising his subject, Boswell – with full permission from Johnson – revealed his flaws, shared his conversations and reported his mannerisms. Such an intimate portrayal had rarely been witnessed before.

Read

Bakewell S. How to Live: A life of Montaigne in one question and twenty attempts at an answer. London: Vintage; 2010.

Hamilton N. Biography: A brief history. Cambridge: Harvard University Press; 2010.

Rollyson C. Essays in Biography. Lincoln: iUniverse; 2005

Sisman A. Boswell's Presumptuous Task: Writing the life of Dr Samuel Johnson. London: Harper Perennial; 2009.

LIVES

The Reading Room frieze

In 1913, Henry Wellcome ordered the names of 30 physicians and scientists to be inscribed around the main gallery of the Wellcome Historical Medical Museum in Wigmore Street (see p. 213). In 1962, the frieze was installed in what is now the Reading Room.

Aristotle (384–322 BCE)

Aristotle
Woodcut from N Reusner's *Icones*, 1589
Tobias Stimmer
586i Wellcome Library

Aristotle is known for his detailed observations on nature and the physical world, which laid the groundwork for the modern study of biology. Among his works are *Physics, Metaphysics, Rhetoric* and *Ethics*.

Avicenna (980–1037)

Avicenna
Engraving
Early 17th century?
M0009341 Wellcome Images

The philosopher–scientist Ibn Sina, or Avicenna, wrote the *Kitab Ash-Shifa* (*Book of Healing*), probably the largest work of its kind authored by a single person. This encyclopaedia of knowledge covered logic, the natural sciences, the quadrivium (geometry, astronomy, arithmetic, music), psychology and metaphysics.

LIVES

Claude Bernard
(1813–78)

Claude Bernard and his pupils
Oil on canvas
Léon-Augustin Lhermitte
45530i Wellcome Library

Bernard was a French physiologist noted for his study of the digestive and nervous systems and the effects of poisons such as carbon monoxide and curare. His concept of the internal environment of the organism led to our present understanding of homeostasis.

Guy de Chauliac
(1300–70)

Guy de Chauliac
Stipple engraving
A Tardieu
3887i Wellcome Library

De Chauliac was a French surgeon and physician at the Papal Court in Avignon. One of the most celebrated surgical writers of the Middle Ages, his major work, *Chirurgia Magna*, remained the principal didactic text on surgery until the eighteenth century.

Hermann Boerhaave
(1668–1738)

Hermann Boerhaave
Line engraving
F Anderloni after G Garavaglia
1210i Wellcome Library

Physician, anatomist, botanist, chemist and humanist, Boerhaave was one of the most influential clinicians and teachers of the eighteenth century. Among his greatest contributions to medicine were the implementation of post-mortems and the use of the Fahrenheit thermometer in clinical assessments.

Charles Darwin
(1809–82)

Charles Darwin
Collotype
M0005668 Wellcome Images

Darwin was an English naturalist and investigator of animal life. He proposed arguments for natural selection as the mode for evolution in his originally controversial book, *On the Origin of Species*.

LIVES

Paul Ehrlich
(1854–1915)

Paul Ehrlich in his laboratory
Photograph
Eduard Blum, *c.*1913
M0017977 Wellcome Images

A German experimental pharmacologist, Ehrlich conducted pioneering research into chemotherapy and developed the chemical Salvarsan for the treatment of syphilis. He shared a 1908 Nobel Prize for his work in the fields of haematology and immunology.

Claudius Galen
(129–200)

Galen
Line engraving
3349i Wellcome Library

Greek philosopher Galen was a physician who worked in Rome. Along with Hippocrates, he is one of the earliest and most frequently cited influences on the development of medicine. Galen is respected for his contributions to anatomy, physiology and pharmacology, and for his incorporation of philosophy, logic and experiment into medicine.

Howard Florey
(1895–1968)

Howard Florey
Photograph
L0012312 Wellcome Images

Florey was an Australian pathologist who introduced penicillin into general medical use. While working with Sir Ernest Boris Chain in 1940, he produced a pure extract of penicillin from *Penicillium notatum*. This work led to the production of sufficient penicillin for the clinical treatment of infections.

Albrecht von Haller
(1708–77)

Baron Albrecht von Haller
Line engraving
3932i Wellcome Library

Swiss Professor of Medicine at Leiden University, von Haller is credited with revolutionising our knowledge of blood flow and heart action. He clarified the relationship between respiration and blood flow, explained nerve action in muscles and developed new insights into reproduction and birth defects.

William Harvey
(1578–1657)

William Harvey
Line engraving
W von Bemmel
4039i Wellcome Library

Harvey was an English physician who proposed evidence for the circulation of blood, as published in *Exercitatio Anatomica de Motu Cordis et Sanguinis in Animalibus (An Anatomical Exercise on the Motion of the Heart and Blood in Animals)*.

John Hunter
(1728–93)

John Hunter
Oil
After Joshua Reynolds
45666i Wellcome Library

Like his brother William Hunter, John Hunter was a surgeon and investigator of animal life. He carried out many important and diverse studies in comparative biology, anatomy, physiology and pathology, and is considered the founder of pathological anatomy in Britain.

Hippocrates
(*c.*460–*c.*380 BCE)

Facsimile of bust of Hippocrates
in the British Museum
L0005203 Wellcome Images

Hippocrates is known as the great ancient Greek physician. He is credited with laying the foundations of medicine as a science and known for his contributions to patients' rights and the moral and professional obligations of physicians (still enshrined in the Hippocratic oath).

William Hunter
(1718–93)

William Hunter
Oil on canvas
45684i Wellcome Library

William Hunter was a Scottish anatomist, physiologist, botanist and antiquarian. He introduced Britain to the French practice of providing individual medical students with cadavers for dissection and worked to establish obstetrics as an accepted branch of medicine.

Edward Jenner
(1749–1823)

Edward Jenner
Pencil with wash
4766i Wellcome Library

English physician and naturalist Jenner introduced vaccination against smallpox. He was also a horticulturist, amateur geologist, zoologist and fossil hunter, even discovering the bones of a plesiosaur in 1819.

Joseph Lister
(1827–1912)

The Right Honourable Joseph Lister
L0002075 Wellcome Images

Lister was an English surgeon who, in 1865, introduced the practice of antisepsis into surgery. His use of carbolic acid decreased postoperative fatalities from infection.

Robert Koch
(1843–1910)

Robert Herman Koch
Photogravure
Anton Mansch, 1906
M0000731 Wellcome Images

German bacteriologist Koch discovered the cholera bacillus and the bacterial cause for anthrax. He won a Nobel Prize in 1905 after discovering the tubercle bacillus (the first bacterium linked to a human disease).

Marcello Malpighi
(1628–94)

Marcello Malpighi
Oil on canvas
45748i Wellcome Library

Regarded by some as the first histologist, Malpighi used the microscope to describe the major types of plant and animal structure. His work marked out key areas of research in botany, embryology, human anatomy and pathology for future generations.

LIVES

Gregor Mendel
(1822–84)

Gregor Mendel
Photogravure
Hugo Iltis, 1932
b10820437 Wellcome Library

Born in Moravia (now the Czech Republic), Mendel is known as the founding father of modern genetics, and is responsible for shaping our understanding of genetic variation.

Paracelsus
(1493–1541)

Paracelsus
Watercolour
9992i Wellcome Library

Swiss alchemist and medical reformer Philippus Aureolus Theophrastus Bombastus von Hohenheim, also known as Paracelsus, is famed for his prolific writings, his achievements in the development of science and his reputation as an alchemist.

Florence Nightingale
(1820–1910)

Florence Nightingale
Coloured lithograph
H M Bonham-Carter, 1854
7449i Wellcome Library

Nightingale was an English pioneer of professionalised nursing and a reformer of hospital sanitation methods. Her organisation and dedication led to a drastic reduction in mortality. She also volunteered to serve in the Crimean War.

Louis Pasteur
(1822–95)

Louis Pasteur
Photograph
Nadar
L0001835 Wellcome Images

French chemist and investigator of animalcules, Pasteur showed the presence of living cells in fermentation in 1864, inventing the process that was named after him: pasteurisation.

LIVES

Ivan Petrovich Pavlov (1849–1936)

Ivan Petrovich Pavlov
Photogravure
After Lafayette Ltd.
13393i Wellcome Library

Pavlov was a Russian experimental physiologist, whose research focused on temperament, conditioning and involuntary reflex actions.

Santiago Ramón y Cajal (1852–1934)

Santiago Ramón y Cajal
Photograph
1928
b10983053 Wellcome Library

Ramón y Cajal was a Spanish histologist who shared a 1906 Nobel Prize with Camillo Golgi for research on the structure of the nervous system.

Philippe Pinel (1745–1826)

Philippe Pinel
Engraving
Lambert after Mme. Mérimée, 1810
7848i Wellcome Library

French nosologist Pinel wrote *Traité Médicophilosophique sur l'Aliénation Mentale, ou la Manie (Medico-Philosophical Treatise on Mental Alienation, or Mania)* in 1801, and established the practice of keeping well-documented psychiatric case histories.

Wilhelm Conrad Roentgen (1845–1923)

Wilhelm Conrad Roentgen
Otto Glasser, 1931
M0010903 Wellcome Images

In 1895, German physicist Roentgen discovered strange rays that were not reflected or refracted. Owing to their mysterious nature, he called them 'X-rays'. He later produced the first X-ray photograph and, in 1901, won the first Nobel Prize for Physics.

LIVES

Susruta
(*c*.800–*c*.600 BCE)

Susruta
Watercolour
H Solomon
M0005328 Wellcome Images

An ancient Indian surgeon and author, Susruta was the originator of plastic surgery, cataract operations, the laparotomy and the vesical lithotomy. He also described diabetes.

Rudolf Virchow
(1821–1902)

Rudolf L K Virchow
Photograph
W Fechner
L0004634 Wellcome Images

Virchow was a German physician, pathologist, anthropologist and politician known for his contributions to cell theory and the study of disease. He established cellular pathology and coined pathological terms such as leucocytosis, leukaemia, neuroglia, thrombosis and amyloid.

Andreas Vesalius
(1514–64)

Andreas Vesalius
Watercolour
9407i Wellcome Library

Regarded as the founder of modern anatomy, Vesalius was a Flemish anatomist, physician and surgeon. In 1543, he authored *De Humani Corporis Fabrica* (*On the Fabric of the Human Body*), which contained the first accurate illustrations of internal human anatomy.

Zhongjing Zhang
(150–219)

Zhongjing Zhang
Painting
1816
L0039825 Wellcome Images

The Chinese author of *Shanghanlung* (*Diseases Caused by External Factors*), Zhang established principles for medication and made a great contribution to the development of traditional Chinese medicine.

LIVES

Henry Wellcome in pictures

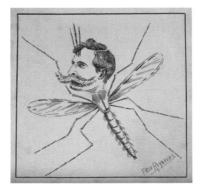

Henry Wellcome caricature
Pen and ink drawing
Fred Reynolds
9590i Wellcome Library

...having travelled so much it is
irksome to remain in one place.

Henry Wellcome writing
to his mother, 8 May 1881

Henry Wellcome aged 16
Photograph
*c.*1869
M0007841 Wellcome Images

Born in a log cabin in northern Wisconsin, USA,
Sir Henry Solomon Wellcome (1853–1936) started
his career working as a travelling salesman for
a New York pharmaceutical company. He died a Knight
of the British Empire, having established himself
as a businessman, collector and philanthropist.

Henry Wellcome in costume
as a warrior
Photograph
1885
M0007861 Wellcome Images

Henry Wellcome (left) and J Bazi, his guide
and interpreter, in Central America
Photograph
1879
L0076781 Wellcome Images

One of the things about Sir Henry
was that he thought he would
never die.

Burroughs Wellcome employee W J Britchford
in a letter dated 29 April 1975

LIVES

The patient perspective

Focusing on the great men (and few women, at least in terms of the Reading Room frieze) of medicine tells only half the story. Medical encounters include the patient as well as the physician, and self-help or community care has as important a role to play in the history of the field as 'professional' medicine.

'The patients with their fears waiting to see the doctor'
Oil on wood
Rosemary Carson, 1997
546554i Wellcome Library

> *The whole world is watching us. Publicity, yes, the newspapers are doing it because they need a story, television is doing it because they need a story, but what about us? We're not stories, we're human beings. Our story needs to be told in our own words, not in the words of the media. If you want to know the truth about Thalidomide, listen to us.*

Sukeshi Thakkar, interviewed in 2013 for *Thalidomide: An oral history*

Pathography on the rise

Professor Anne Hunsaker Hawkins defines pathography as 'a form of autobiography or biography that describes personal experiences of illness, treatment and sometimes death'. As a literary genre, pathography only really emerged in the late twentieth century. In her book *Reconstructing Illness*, Hawkins attributes this to the modern separation of illness and everyday life, and a contemporary medical focus on disease rather than the patient experience. Pathography, Hawkins says, 'returns the voice of the patient to the world of medicine' and can be seen as the counterpart to the story presented by the physician's case.

> *...I awoke with a chilly fit. A violent fever with acute pains in different parts of my body followed it... I saw my danger painted in [my pupil's] countenance. He bled me plentifully and gave me a dose of the mercurial medicine... The remaining part of the night was passed under an apprehension that my labours were near an end.*

Dr Benjamin Rush describing his own experience of contracting 'bilious remitting yellow fever' in Philadelphia, 1793

Read

Brody H. Stories of Sickness. New York: Oxford University Press; 2002.

Hawkins AH. Reconstructing Illness: Studies in pathography. Indiana: Purdue University Press; 1998.

Marsh H. Do No Harm: Stories of life, death and brain surgery. London: Weidenfeld & Nicolson; 2014.

Sacks O. The Man who Mistook his Wife for a Hat. London: Picador; 2011.

Watt B. Patient: The true story of a rare illness. London: Viking; 1996.

> *...the best teaching is that taught by the patient.*

Sir William Osler in *On the Need of a Radical Reform in Our Methods of Teaching Medical Students*, 1904

LIVES

A second opinion

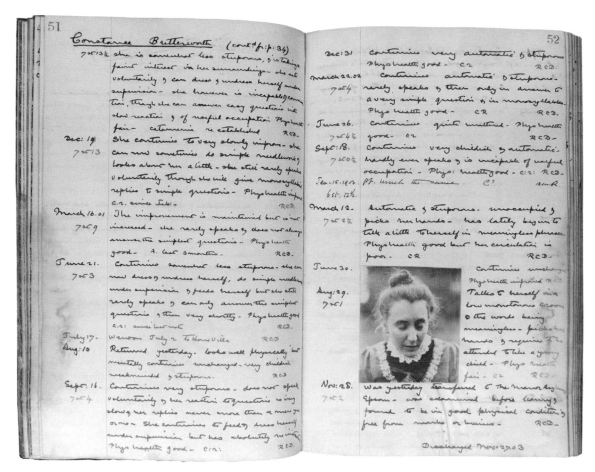

Medical case history of Constance Butterworth, a patient of Holloway Sanatorium
L0033810 Wellcome Images

Physicians are themselves biographers of individual patients, whose narratives they construct in case notes and histories. Describing patients as 'presenting with' specific circumstances or symptoms, medical case notes inherently acknowledge the distinction between the patient's own story and the physician's interpretation (or diagnosis) of it. Developing from a combination of the physician's prior medical knowledge and the expression of disease in the individual they are treating, these stories often have multiple plot lines. Patients who demand a second opinion could be considered as characters hoping to discover an alternative ending to their own story.

RIGHT: **Constance Butterworth Photograph from** *Holloway Sanatorium Hospital for the Insane, Virginia Water, Surrey, Females no. 11: Certified female patients admitted May 1898–May 1899*
L0049042 Wellcome Images

Holy water flasks
19th–20th century

Faith

Faith and spirituality are intensely personal issues, which are experienced and expressed in many different ways. Faith isn't restricted to belief in a religious doctrine. More broadly, it encompasses the placing of trust and confidence in a being, object or philosophy, whether real or imagined. The very human desire to believe in something is fed by a hunger for explanations and a need for safety, security and future well-being.

For some, petitions to gods and saints, or reliance on amulets and charms, may deliver meaning, reduce anxiety and strengthen bonds with others. In the increasingly secular societies of many Western countries, belief in humanism, political ideologies or science may instead provide comfort, along with powerful explanations of the world. In fact, belief in science has been seen to increase when non-religious people are placed in threatening situations.

Historically, faith and medicine were intrinsically linked. Inmates in the earliest hospitals, which were attached to priories and monasteries, attended confession and prayed for their salvation. Illness was seen as a divine action that might prompt guilt about the sins it was thought to be punishing, or joy for the ultimate good it would result in for the soul. Of course, ill health may also test people of faith, who may question why they or their loved ones are suffering.

Contemporary research suggests that beliefs and expectations associated with therapeutic procedures play an important role in health, as demonstrated by the power of the placebo response. However, placebos may also mask or prevent some beneficial health interventions; negative suggestions of their impact can also lead to negative outcomes.

...there are many occasions, in the general round of daily life, when magic is attempted by the ordinary man – though usually, indeed, without a thought of it as such – in the wearing of an amulet, for example...or the use of some word or formula to guard against the evil believed to follow upon some inauspicious speech or act.

Dr Walter Hildburgh in *Japanese Household Magic*, 1908

Holy water flasks

**Holy water flasks
19th–20th century**
RRa0118 / Science Museum / Wellcome Images

In the Catholic church, water becomes 'holy' once it has been blessed by an ordained minister. By sprinkling or anointing, holy water is used to bless people, objects and places. It plays a key role in sacraments such as baptism and is used in exorcisms; it has also been employed as protection against vampires and witches.

In medieval times, holy water was used in medicinal treatments. According to preacher Bernadino of Siena (1380–1444), it offered 'a thousand remedies against demons and temptations and plague and sickness and every diabolical affliction and against every danger'.

FAITH

Holy water flask

Holy water flask
Painted glass
RRa0118.2 / A77269 Science Museum / L0076064
Wellcome Images

Holy water flask

Holy water flask
Painted glass
Late 19th–early 20th century
RRa0118.7 / A660684 Science Museum / L0076077
Wellcome Images

Holy water flask

Holy water flask
Hand-painted glass
RRa0118.4 / A77267 Science Museum / L0076068
Wellcome Images

📎 With added worms

In 2001, the *British Medical Journal* ran a news story about three 14-year-old girls from County Kildare in Ireland who examined holy water from fonts at local churches as part of a Young Scientist contest. The girls chose their subject because one of them had developed a rash on her forehead after anointing herself with holy water. They found large quantities of dirt in many of the fonts they studied, and green worms about half a centimetre long in one sample.

> *For elf-sickness, take bishop's-wort, fennel, lupin, alfthone the lower part and lichen from a hallowed crucifix and frankincense, put a handful of each, tie up all the herbs in a cloth, dip in consecrated font-water three times, let sing over them three masses...*

Bald's Leechbook, c.950

Holy water flasks featuring St Nicholas

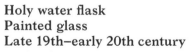

Holy water flask
Glass
Late 19th–early 20th century
RR0118.11 / A660489 Science Museum / L0076087
Wellcome Images

Holy water flask
Painted glass
Late 19th–early 20th century
RRa0118.8 / A660614 Science Museum / L0076081
Wellcome Images

This flask painted with the image of St Nicholas
(270–343) may come from the basilica in Bari, Italy,
where the saint's remains are claimed to lie. On
9 May every year, the 'manna of St Nicholas' – water
that forms in his tomb – is collected during a special
mass. Amounting to no more than 50 ml in volume,
this 'pure' water is mixed with holy water and sold
in decorated glass bottles as a curative drink.

Holy water flask
Painted glass
19th century
RRa0118.14 / A660480 Science Museum / L0076094
Wellcome Images

FAITH

Holy water flask
Hand-painted glass
Late 19th–early 20th century
RRa0118.5 / A660496 Science Museum / L0076069
Wellcome Images

Holy water flask
Hand-painted glass
RRa0118.1 / A660494 Science Museum / L0076061
Wellcome Images

Holy water flask
Hand-painted glass
Late 19th–early 20th century
RRa0118.6 / A660490 Science Museum / L0076074
Wellcome Images

📎 Controlling springs

The symbolic properties of water – with its purifying, life-giving qualities and its opposition to evil and ill-health – are central to the hugely popular French film *Jean de Florette* (1986) and its sequel *Manon des Sources*. In the film, the 'evil' characters Ugolin and Cesar block the natural spring belonging to the 'good' incomer Jean, leading indirectly to the latter's death. When Jean's daughter discovers that the villagers knew about the spring but remained silent, she in turn blocks up the spring that feeds the village well.

📎 2000-year-old vending machine

Writer and inventor Hero of Alexandria developed a coin-operated vending machine for holy water in the first century. Dropping a coin in a slot pivoted a lever and opened a vessel that allowed the water to flow. When the coin reached a certain point, another lever would be triggered, which cut off the flowing water.

FAITH

Holy water flask with a bed

Holy water flask with a bed
Painted glass
RRa0118.3 / A77266 Science Museum / L0076065
Wellcome Images

Holy water flask

Holy water flask
Glass
Late 19th–early 20th century
RRa0118.10 / A660476/1 Science Museum / L0076086
Wellcome Images

Holy water flask

Holy water flask
Painted glass
Late 19th–early 20th century
RRa0118.9 / A660477 Science Museum / L0076083
Wellcome Images

Holy water flask

Holy water flask
Painted glass
Late 19th–early 20th century
RRa0118.12 / A660486 Science Museum / L0076089
Wellcome Images

FAITH

Holy water flask

Holy water flask
Painted glass
Late 19th–early 20th century
RRa0118.13 / A660491 Science Museum / L0076091
Wellcome Images

Ø Dissolving witches

The Wicked Witch of the West in L Frank Baum's
1900 novel *The Wonderful Wizard of Oz* is apparently
undone by the purifying quality of water. When
Dorothy throws a bucket of water over her (deliberately
in the novel, inadvertently in the 1939 film version),
the witch melts away and disappears forever.

Ø 'Swimming' witches

The practice of immersing suspected witches in 'pure'
water, which was thought to reject (or prevent from
drowning) those who were guilty, was advocated
by King James I and VI in his 1597 book *Daemonologie*.
'Swimming' was later considered such a definitive test
for witchcraft that the accused often demanded
it in order to clear their names.

☐ Read

Bradley I. Water: A spiritual history. London:
    Bloomsbury; 2012.
Pavlac BA. Witch Hunts in the Western World:
    Persecution and punishment from the inquisition
    through the Salem trials. Westport: Greenwood
    Press; 2009.

Ø Baptism water

Water collected from the River Jordan
Jordan, 1920–30
A6033, A6034 Science Museum / L0057065 Wellcome
Images

Pilgrims who travel to the river Jordan site where
Jesus Christ is believed to have been baptised by
John the Baptist may collect and take away samples
of river water. The liquid has perceived medicinal
and health-giving qualities, but is also a souvenir
of the trip.

> *I have long preserved a phial of*
> *water from the Jordan for the*
> *christening of my first grandson,*
> *should it please God to grant*
> *me one... Small matters like this*
> *sometimes influence a child's*
> *whole future career.*
>
> George Pontifex in Samuel Butler's novel
> *The Way of All Flesh*, 1903

📎 A giant holy dip

Bathing and praying in the Ganges
Gouache on mica
19th century
580864i Wellcome Library

On 10 February 2013, over 30 million people bathed at the confluence of the Ganges and Yamuna rivers in India, believing that praying and taking to the water on that specific day would wash away their sins. The mass pilgrimage was part of the Hindu Kumbh Mela festival, the largest religious gathering in the world, which takes place every 12 years. Pilgrims also carry holy Ganges water away with them.

...my design is to shew which [waters] are sickly, and which healthy; and what sort of disorders are to be expected, and what sort of advantages, from 'em: For the share they have in the affair of Health is very great.

Hippocrates in *Airs, Waters, Places*, from Francis Clifton's 1784 edition

📎 Sipping cement, relics and blood

Until the twelfth century, Christian churches supplied pilgrims with water that had been in contact with the remains of saints. These healing mixtures might contain cement scraped from tombs, water that had washed over sarcophagi, or liquid in which a relic of the True Cross had been dipped. In Canterbury, the 'Water of St Thomas' cure-all was dispensed from a cistern containing the much-diluted blood of the martyr St Thomas Becket.

📖 Read

Salzman J. Drinking Water: A history. New York: Overlook Duckworth; 2012.

Varner GR. Sacred Wells: A study in the history, meaning, and mythology of holy wells and waters. New York: Algora Publishing; 2009.

Harrington A. The Cure Within: A history of mind–body medicine. New York: WW Norton; 2008.

Ross AI. The Anthropology of Alternative Medicine. London: Berg; 2012.

FAITH

High water

As its title suggests, Hippocrates's fourth-century treatise on *Airs, Waters, Places* includes much discussion of the health benefits of water. Written as a guide for itinerant physicians, the work recommends assessing a range of environmental factors when first arriving at a new location, in order to master 'the particular diseases of the place'. Hippocrates considered that the best waters came from 'high places and hilly grounds'.

The myth of Bath

Stories of holy wells with the power to heal the sick are common around the world. Legend has it that the curative waters of Bath spa were found by the leprous son of a ninth-century BCE West-country king. According to a twelfth-century tale recounted in John Wood's 1765 *An Essay Toward a Description of Bath*, the unfortunate youth became a swineherd after he was banished from his home. His pigs became infected with his own sores, but were cured when they wallowed in the mud at a place where the ground never froze. When the swineherd immersed himself in the spot, he was saved; he returned to his family and later became king. He then founded the city of Bath at the site of his cure. This mythical story emphasises both the physical and social healing aspects of Bath's waters.

Ruins of Roman baths at Bath
Photograph
1844
L0002624 Wellcome Images

The meaning of healing

Despite ongoing debates about the placebo response, a treatment cannot be separated from the meaning wrapped up in the interaction between the medical practitioner and patient, and the overall cultural context in which this encounter takes place. Research has shown that the level of empathy displayed by medical staff significantly affects the outcomes of chronic diseases.

The power of suggestion is also clear: numerous studies report that believing a treatment will have a benefit (even if there is no intrinsic benefit in it) leads to more positive outcomes. Aside from their obvious appeal to adept advertisers, these findings prompt a fundamental ethical question around the administering of placebos without informing the patient.

A man self-administering hydrotherapy
Lithograph with watercolour
11898i Wellcome Library

The text on this lithograph says: 'Cure for a fever: sit in the water but and let the spout run on your head till you feel better.'

'A Woman in Bed in a Sick Room'

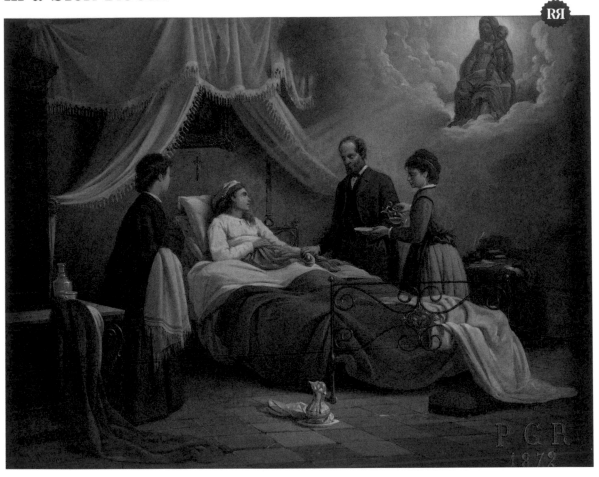

'A Woman in Bed in a Sick Room'
Oil on canvas
R Pistoni, 1872

RRa0096 / 44870i Wellcome Library

The physician in this scene may be playing a role in his patient's recovery, but the painting was produced in gratitude to the Madonna del Parto, shown overseeing the situation from above. An ex-voto offering made to fulfil a vow to Our Lady of Childbirth, the painting's 'P G R' inscription stands for *per grazia ricevuta* (meaning 'for grace received'). Votive offerings such as this come in all shapes and sizes, and are often placed at shrines.

> *I have rarely seen a shrine adorned by so many votive offerings. On her own person are displayed jewels of every sort. Her fingers are literally covered with rings, and round her neck I have counted eighteen necklaces of rubies, pearls, and coral; sundry watches were also hung about her person. The other votive offerings are attached to the adjoining walls of the church, and cover several hundred square feet.*

A description of the Madonna del Parto statue in Rome, from the *Christian Guardian and Church of England Magazine*, 1833

FAITH

Placenta votive offering
Baked clay
Roman, 200 BCE–200 CE
A635557 Science Museum / L0058478 Wellcome Images

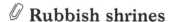

🖉 Rubbish shrines

Folk saints can have as devoted followings as their canonised counterparts, and are honoured at numerous shrines littered with votive offerings. One of Argentina's most-favoured folk saints is Difunta Correa ('the deceased Correa'). A legendary woman from the nineteenth century, Correa reportedly walked into the desert with her baby to search for her husband, who had been forced into the army during a civil war. Though Correa died of dehydration, her baby was found alive, suckling from her mother's breast, which miraculously continued to produce milk. The most common offerings to Correa are water bottles and car tyres, lending her shrines the inauspicious look of a rubbish tip.

🖉 Votive charms

These body parts were hung around shrines to wish for a cure relating to the part of the body they represent. They might also be offered as a token of thanks after recovery.

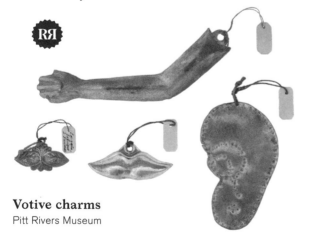

Votive charms
Pitt Rivers Museum

Surgeon, assistants and patient
all praying before an operation
From *Schnitt-und Augenarztes*, 1559
Caspar Stomayr
M0010143 Wellcome Images

My comfort is in Christ; I pray you trouble me not with the Physician... Jesus Christ will be my Physician: for my grave is better for me then to be here. Again, Lord reveal unto me what is the cause of this affliction, what sin it is that lies unrepented of; sins of omission, or commission, or what sins soever they are; Lord, reveal them to me, and pardon them all, and give me repentance for them; with many such words which are not remembered... Again, Oh my sin is the cause of it; Oh teach me to say as David, It is good for me that I have been afflicted.

11-year-old Martha Hatfield after the onset
of distemper of the spleen, reported in James
Fisher's *The Wise Virgin*, 1653

🖹 Read

Porterfield A. Healing in the History of Christianity.
New York: Oxford University Press; 2005.

'Life and Death'

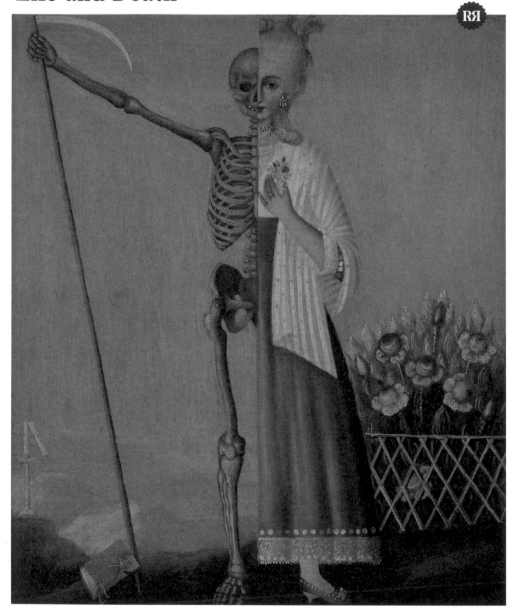

'Life and Death'
Oil on canvas
Artist and date unknown
RRa0095 / 45063i Wellcome Library

This *vanitas* painting was designed to keep death present in people's minds. A reminder of the transience of life, it acts as a moralising warning to refrain from indulging in earthly pleasures and a prompt to do good while still alive. It would, of course, backfire if its viewer didn't believe in life after death; they might instead be encouraged to enjoy themselves while they can.

🔍 Symbols of transience

The broken candle, like other common *vanitas* motifs, symbolises the transient nature of life. Images of skulls, hourglasses, bones and glasses (half empty or tipped over) serve similar purposes. In contemporary art, this symbolism has been taken to a new level by Marc Quinn (see p. 80), whose 'Self' self-portrait is cast from his own frozen blood. Quinn makes a new version of the sculpture every five years, documenting his own transformation and deterioration.

FAITH

Embracing death

Vanitas tableau
Wax
18th century

A99821 Science Museum / L0035771 Wellcome Images

To the Christian...death does not come as a surprise, because he has learned to carry 'memento mori' into the midst of life, and can thus turn even death into something that he does, not merely that he suffers, and make it a work of willing and joyful surrender. He goes from this earthly scene, he is not dragged from it like a prisoner.

Isaak August Dorner and August Johannes Dorner in *System of Christian Ethics*, 1887

The redundant scythe

Personifications of death as the Grim Reaper, an animate skeleton often cloaked in a black hooded cowl, invariably feature the figure carrying a scythe, with which to harvest souls. However, the Reaper usually does his job simply by appearing; he is a herald, with a solely symbolic scythe, rather than the being that physically takes someone's life.

Winged skeleton holding a scythe
Etching

36594i Wellcome Library

Death on film

The Grim Reaper that has saturated religious art for centuries has inevitably flowed into popular culture. In Ingmar Bergman's *The Seventh Seal* (1957), a crusader knight plays chess with a black-clad Death in the hope that it will forestall his own end. Meanwhile, the Grim Reaper's comic potential has also been richly explored; in his 1975 film *Love and Death*, Woody Allen (a Bergman devotee) encounters Death as a white-clad figure with a hidden face and doom-laden voice. In a childhood flashback, the young Allen character questions Death: 'What happens after we die? Is there a hell? Is there a god?… Are there girls?'

Read

Llewellyn N. The Art of Death: Visual culture in the English death ritual *c.*1500–1800. London: Reaktion Books; 1991.

Townsend C. Art and Death. London: IB Tauris; 2008.

Townsend E. Death and Art: Europe 1200–1530. London: V&A Publishing; 2009.

Watkins C. The Undiscovered Country: Journeys among the dead. London: Bodley Head; 2013.

FAITH

'Saint Expeditus'

'Saint Expeditus'
Oil on canvas
Italy, 19th century
RRa0015 / 47484i Wellcome Library

This banner, designed to be carried in procession, depicts St Expeditus, a Roman centurion based in Armenia, who was beheaded in the fourth century. Praying to Expeditus is thought to 'expedite' success in many areas, including trade, examinations, lawsuits and health.

🔍 Don't put off until tomorrow

Expeditus's commitment to getting things done rather than postponing them is explicit in his trampling of the crow, who squawks 'CRAS' (tomorrow), while holding up a cross bearing the word 'HODIE' (today).

**A domestic shrine with 66 Shinto
and Buddhist deities
19th century**

A199221 Science Museum / L0043822 Wellcome Images

In Japanese domestic life, worshippers of these gods seek concrete rewards on Earth rather than outcomes in the afterlife. Petitions often request physical healing as well as financial or personal success.

The saint of shipping?

An appealing myth about the popularisation of St Expeditus revolves around the story of a nineteenth-century community of Parisian nuns who received a package from Rome containing relics of a martyr. Interpreting the Italian word *Spedito* (meaning 'ships') written on the shipping crate to be the name of its contents, the nuns are said to have Latinised the word to *Expeditus*. The story reappears in different forms to explain how the Expeditus cult was shipped to New Orleans and the Indian Ocean island of Réunion, both locations where he is a popular saint.

An offering of pound cake

St Expeditus is also a popular voodoo spirit, called on to help settle disputes or satisfy pressing needs. In New Orleans, it is customary to offer Expeditus pound cake (particularly of the Sara Lee brand), flowers and a glass of water.

Remover of obstacles

The elephant-headed Hindu god Ganesh is known as the remover of obstacles and bestower of success. Devotees worship him to smooth the road before embarking on a long journey or a new venture.

**Ganesh playing the dhola drum
Watercolour
1890**

582942i Wellcome Library

'Saint Cosmas and Saint Damian in a Landscape'

**'Saint Cosmas and Saint Damian
in a Landscape'**
Oil on canvas
Spain, 17th century
RRa0097 / 44852i Wellcome Library

The third-century Christian physicians Cosmas and Damian (see p. 132) are shown here holding a urine flask and a spatula and ointment box.

The twin brothers were martyred for their faith, beheaded during Roman emperor Diocletian's persecution of Christians.

FAITH

Heroic suffering

Elizabeth of Hungary (1207–31), the daughter of King Andrew II, is another healing saint, associated with hospital care and nursing. In a controversial 1931 reappraisal of her story, German historian Elisabeth Busse-Wilson (1890–1974) identified Elizabeth's saintliness with the masculine ideal of maternal nurturing and redefined her namesake's religious devotion as a suicidal determination to seek out her own death. As Busse-Wilson wrote, 'the Christian legend has only one standard for greatness: heroic suffering'.

Saint Elizabeth offering food and drink to a patient
Oil on copper
Adam Elsheimer, 1598
44650i Wellcome Library

Read

Giorgi R. Saints and Their Symbols. New York: Abrams; 2012.

De Voraigne J. The Golden Legend: Readings on the saints. New Jersey: Princeton University Press; 2012.

Zaleski P, Zaleski C. Prayer: A history. New York: Mariner Press; 2006.

A medicine vendor kneeling and praying
Coloured etching
T Rowlandson after G Woodward, 1801
20936i Wellcome Library

This medicine vendor is praying to Richard Rock (1690–1777), a quack (see p. 28) famous for his 'anti-venereal, grand, specific pill'. The prayer includes the lines 'deign to continue to me my carriage and equipage, my town and country residence, and all other good things of this life, and thy humble petitioner shall ever praise thee'.

Unified in prayer

When African-American human-rights activist and minister for the Nation of Islam Malcolm X (1925–65) travelled to Mecca in 1964, he experienced the unifying power of prayer. In a letter to his followers in the Harlem district of New York, Malcolm X wrote of eating, drinking, sleeping and praying with 'fellow Muslims, whose eyes were the bluest of blue, whose hair was the blondest of blonde, and whose skin was the whitest of white'. Viewing these Muslims as 'truly all the same (brothers)', he considered that their shared belief in one God had 'removed the white from their minds, the white from their behaviour, and the white from their attitude'.

Muslims praying to Mecca
Engraving
11514i Wellcome Library

Amulets and charms

Primarily it is the retention of the object, for the sake of its presumed apotropaic, medicinal, or magical virtues, which marks it as an amulet...

Walter Hildburgh writing in *Folklore*, 1951

Amulets made from animals or animal parts
Pitt Rivers Museum

Any object can become a protective amulet or good-luck charm, so long as its owner believes (or hopes) it has the power to affect the world around them. Just as the value of an object in a museum collection is transformed from its intrinsic natural or functional purpose into something more representational, amulets are redefined and repurposed by those who use and value them. Derived from the Arabic term *hamala*, which means 'to carry', most amulets are worn in some way, or kept in bags or pockets.

The amulets and charms on display in the Reading Room were collected by three different individuals. Their original owners employed them as protection against threats such as the 'evil eye', or hoped they would bring fertility, good health and good luck. For full details on each amulet, please consult the dedicated *Amulets, charms and votives* booklet.

Twig used as an amulet for long life
Ash
RRa0164 / 1985.51.230 Pitt Rivers Museum

FAITH

📎 Contemporary amulets

To accompany Wellcome Collection's 2011 exhibition *Charmed Life: The solace of objects*, anthropologist Nathalia Bruchet took to the streets of London to discover whether present-day Londoners carried amulets. Though they may not have defined them as such, Bruchet's interviewees kept or carried charm bracelets, milk teeth, stones, brooches and pieces of paper. These highly personalised objects made their owners feel safe, secure and hopeful, and would cause anxiety if lost. One of the interviewees worried, however, about developing unhealthy attachments to objects, which might become encumbrances.

Edward Lovett

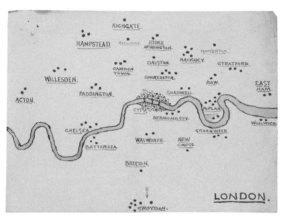

London districts where blue amulet necklaces were collected
Sketch
Edward Lovett, 1914

L0051628 Wellcome Images

Edward Lovett (1852–1933), a bank clerk in the City of London, lived in Croydon but spent his spare time visiting working-class areas of London to collect material from herbalists, costermongers and dock workers. His 1916 exhibition *The Folklore of London* was held in the Wellcome Historical Medical Museum and he later published *Magic of Modern London*, now available as a Wellcome mobile app.

...for the seeker after amulets, there is no better hunting ground than the hawkers' handbarrows in the poorest parts or slums of such dense aggregations of people as London, Rome, and Naples.

Edward Lovett writing in *Folklore*, 1909

Lovett considered that researchers 'of folk-beliefs and articles connected with them' met with far more difficulties than other collectors, since ardent believers might be averse to exposing 'sacred things' to an outsider. Unbelievers might also be reluctant to share information about superstitions they thought degrading. Lovett himself was dismissive about the idea that amulets could work as magical objects.

Blue glass beads
UK

RRa0178 / 1985.51.72 Pitt Rivers Museum

Around the time of World War I, blue necklaces like this were put around the necks of working-class London children to be worn as preventative charms against bronchitis. They were never removed – even for washing – and remained on the body after death.

...many things which by our definition are amulets are to their users merely medicines just as simple and as natural in their actions as the decoctions of roots and herbs... Should an inquirer ask merely about 'amulets' in use, he is likely to be given little information... Should, however, the inquirer ask concerning medicines which are to be carried or kept, he will be far more likely to get information of the very sort he seeks...

Walter Hildburgh writing in *Folklore*, 1951

📖 Read

Roud S. London Lore: The legends and traditions of the world's most vibrant city. London: Arrow Books; 2010.

FAITH

Concealed shoes

![RR]

Shoe amulets and charms
Pitt Rivers Museum

Since at the least the fourteenth century, single, worn shoes have been concealed in English buildings, often near the fireplace or chimney, as a protection against evil forces and bad luck.

....

📖 Read

Paine S. Amulets: A world of secret powers. London: Thames & Hudson; 2004.

💬

Of all objects which in any way appeal to the imagination from the point of view of superstition, or sentiment, or what you will, there is nothing stronger or so directly forcible as a shoe. Its symbolism, as well as its delightful sentiment, is so simple, so logical, and yet so full, really of poetry, that it appeals to all...

Edward Lovett in *Magic in Modern London*, 1925

FAITH

Seahorses

Glass seahorse and miniature aluminium gondola prow
Italy
RRa0174, RRa0188 / 1985.51.538, 1985.51.871
Pitt Rivers Museum

When I was in Venice,
one of the first things that struck
me was that every gondola had
a brass sea horse on each
gunwale, and facing the bow...
I am very much inclined to believe
that the curious white metal prow
of this remarkable boat is evolved
from the sea horse...

Edward Lovett in *Magic in Modern London*, 1925

Three dried seahorses
Italy
RRa0169 / 1985.51.340 Pitt Rivers Museum

In *Magic in Modern London*, Edward Lovett related finding itinerant hawkers selling seahorses 'tied in bundles of three with red worsted' on the Venice Lido. At the nearby town of Chioggia, he found fishermen's wives, who kept dried seahorses on their breasts to facilitate the flow of milk while nursing infants.

Bawdy charms

In the Middle Ages, it was common for pilgrims to acquire small metal badges from the shrines they visited, in part to protect from harm and to bring good luck. While many depicted saints and other religious symbols, some have been found with far bawdier imagery, including male and female genitalia in the most unusual of 'tableaux', such as an ambulant female vulva with legs, sporting a hat and carrying a staff.

Adrien de Mortillet

Adrien de Mortillet holding a skull
Photograph
13593i Wellcome Library

When Adrien de Mortillet (1853–1931) was 19, he left France for Moscow, where he took a job in a French perfume factory and became a circus juggler and aeronaut. After completing his military service for France, he worked with his father Gabriel, a famous anthropologist and archaeologist, illustrating many of his books. De Mortillet himself later became a lecturer in anthropology and travelled to South America as principal archaeologist on a government expedition. He sold his amulet collection to the Wellcome Museum a few months before he died; the amulets from de Mortillet's collection still have his original tiny green labels attached.

FAITH

Fertile herds

Animal *illas*
Alabaster
Bolivia
Pitt Rivers Museum

De Mortillet bought several *illas* — animals carved from Andean alabaster stone — when he travelled to Tiahuanaco, Bolivia in 1903. Carried by herders in small bags with coca leaves, these llamas and oxen were thought to protect animals and bring them fertility. In turn, this would deliver prosperity for their human keepers.

Four rams, one facing in the opposite direction
Alabaster
Bolivia
RRa00261 / 1985.52.1866 Pitt Rivers Museum

Protective hands

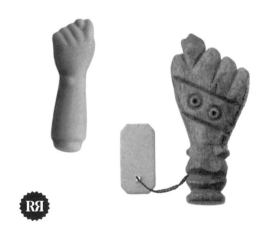

Blue glass and bone 'fig hands'
France and Italy
RRa0212, RRa0151 / 1985.50.1215, 1985.52.932
Pitt Rivers Museum

Common in France, Italy and Spain, these 'fig hands' are also known as *mano ficas* or *higas*. They have been used since Roman and Phoenician times as protection against the 'evil eye'. In the Muslim world, open palms known as 'hands of Fatima' (named after Muhammad's daughter) serve the same purpose. In fifteenth-century Spain, they were sewn on to the shoulders of children's clothing.

FAITH

**A Cairo woman reputed
to possess the evil eye
Photograph**
M0005596 Wellcome Images

**'Extruding Coral'
Wax on mirror back
Felicity Powell, 2011**
Felicity Powell / Wellcome Images

Coral as a substance is thought to protect against the
evil eye, whatever shape it is carved into.

The hand of marriage

Suitors in Bavaria and Austria would, at one time,
present a fig hand made of silver to the object of their
affection. If accepted, the girl would attach the hand
to her bodice and give, in return, a silver hand holding
a heart, to be worn on a watch-chain.

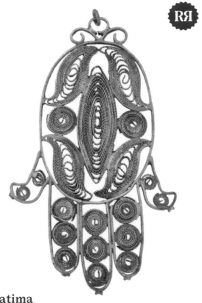

**Hand of Fatima
Silver filigree
Tunisia**
RRa00214 / 1985.50.1201 Pitt Rivers Museum

Sporting charms

The ritualistic use of lucky charms is a well-known
phenomenon amongst elite sportsmen and women.
American basketball superstar Michael Jordan reportedly always wore his University of North Carolina
shorts underneath his Chicago Bulls team kit while
Swedish tennis giant Björn Borg always grew a beard
before Wimbledon and wore the same Fila shirt.
The French football team treated goalkeeper Fabien
Barthez as a human talisman throughout the 1998
World Cup; before kickoff in every match, Laurent
Blanc would kiss Barthez's shaven pate. France
won the tournament, for the first time in the nation's
history.

Read

Dundes A (ed). The Evil Eye: A casebook. Madison:
University of Wisconsin Press; 1992.
Elworthy FT. The Evil Eye: The classic account
of an ancient superstition, Vol.1. Mineola, NY:
Dover; 2004.

FAITH

Walter Hildburgh

Daruma doll
Pottery
Japan
RRa00248 / 1985.53.740 Pitt Rivers Museum

New York-born Walter Leo Hildburgh (1876–1955) trained as a scientist and competed in international figure-skating competitions before becoming a respected collector and art historian. In 1912 he moved to London, where he frequented the Victoria and Albert Museum, to which he donated a major collection. Hildburgh also studied folklore, anthropology and magic. He travelled widely, spending a large amount of time in Japan.

Hildburgh referred to himself as a 'locust collector', since he bought up every amulet he found. His passions for learning and sharing his knowledge were, however, as strong as his desire to collect.

The instinct to seek protection is...particularly strong in human kind, with its long infancy and the protracted childhood in which that instinct is reinforced through experience and reason.

Walter Hildburgh writing
in *Folklore*, 1951

Beckoning good luck

Beckoning cat
Japan
RRa00243 / 1985.53.709 Pitt Rivers Museum

The Japanese *maneki-neko*, or 'beckoning cat', s a contemporary talismanic figurine believed to bring good fortune to its owner. The cats are usually stationed at the entrance to shops or in the home, with one paw raised (and if battery-powered, the paw moves up and down in a beckoning gesture). The raised paw is believed to attract customers, and bring good luck and wealth.

🗋 Read

Ashkenazi M. Handbook of Japanese Mythology. Oxford: Oxford University Press; 2008.
Mack J. The Art of Small Things. London: British Museum Press; 2007.

FAITH

Anti-choking pigeons

Plaster pigeons
Japan
RRa00239 / 1985.53.687 Pitt Rivers Museum

In Hildburgh's time, small representations of pigeons were commonly found at the Asakusa Temple in Tokyo, where they were sold as a *majinai* (or charm) against choking. Setting them out at every meal, the diner would offer each item of food to the birds with their chopsticks before eating it. Hildburgh attributed their 'power' to the fact that live pigeons have very large throats and are never choked by their food. More pragmatically, he also pointed out that taking the time to offer food to the birds would force people to eat slowly, therefore reducing the risk of choking.

💬

...if a Man carries a Planets Seal, or a Ring, or some Part of a Beast, believing strongly, that it will help him to obtain his Love; or to keep him from danger of hurt in Fight; or to prevail in a Sute; &c. it may make him more Active, and Industrious; and again, more Confident and Persisting, than otherwise he would be.

English philosopher Francis Bacon
in *Sylva Sylvarum*, 1626

Christian themes

Galvanic battery
France
RRa0149 / 1985.52.777 Pitt Rivers Museum

By shaping this electromagnetic amulet into a cross, it has been given what Hildburgh described as 'an atmosphere of piety'. Writing in 1955, Hildburgh reported that the church in Spain had deliberately tried to 'wean the persons in their care from the use of secular amulets', with the intention of attributing amulets' preservative or curative virtues to small crosses instead.

...amulets, though fundamentally magical, tend to take religion as an aid and ally, just as the converse is often true: and wherever amulets are made with the help of the graphic and plastic arts, they are likely to invoke, by their design and inscriptions, the support of local divinities, and to absorb into themselves local religious ideas...

Campbell Bonner, an American scholar of Greek, writing in the *Harvard Theological Review*, 1946

FAITH

'Apotheosis
of an Ecclesiastic'

'Apotheosis of an Ecclesiastic'
Oil on canvas
Italian, date unknown
RRa0098 / 44815i Wellcome Library

The ecclesiastic taking centre stage under the phrase 'protection and glory' is being elevated to divine status, the ultimate glory for a mortal.

🖉 Gods as emperors

In ancient Rome, men could become divine as a result of their great deeds. As soon as the Roman senate deified Julius Caesar (100–44 BCE) after his death, his adopted son Octavian (63 BCE–14 CE) referred to himself as the son of a god, and the letters D F (standing for *divi filius* or 'son of the divine') were attached to his name on inscriptions and coins.

Octavian soon rose to greater heights, though: when he became the emperor Augustus, the Roman poets compared him to a god, or referred to him directly as one. Outside Rome, he was worshipped as a living god, presaging his own official deification after his death.

Julius Caesar
Engraving
**After Aegidius Sadeler, after Titian,
18th century**
664532i Wellcome Library

🖉 The divine nurse

When British nurse Edith Cavell (1865–1915) was executed by a German firing squad after admitting to 'assisting men to the enemy' during World War I, the Allies claimed her as a martyr. Cavell herself wouldn't have approved; when a chaplain who saw her the night before her death suggested she would be remembered as a heroine and a martyr, Cavell replied that she should be thought of only as 'a nurse who tried to do her duty'.

And the ages that are to come will learn her name. Yes, long after other great actors in this awful tragedy are forgotten – when the names of kings and kaisers are lost in the obscurity of the past – the sacrifice made by Edith Cavell will be remembered as we remember the holy deeds of saints and the martyrdom of the Christian virgins.

Rev. Lord William Cecil's sermon about Edith Cavell in the *Daily Telegraph*

RIGHT: **Edith Cavell's spirit rises from her dead body in the form of an angel**
Lithograph
1915

547652i Wellcome Library

📎 Worshipping idols

'Modern Idolatry – or – editors and idols'
Etching with watercolour
Charles Williams, 1814

38402i Wellcome Library

This nineteenth-century etching represents the sycophancy of the press by depicting a number of well-known journalists sitting by the feet of 'idols', who are public figures of the day.

📖 Read

Ellenbogen J, Tugendhaft A (eds). Idol Anxiety. Stanford: Stanford University Press; 2011.

Rupke J. A Companion to Roman Religion. Oxford: Blackwell Publishing; 2011.

Souhami D. Edith Cavell. London: Quercus; 2011.

FAITH

Hall of Statuary stairs

Wellcome's library

Henry Wellcome's passion for collecting is impossible to deny, but his relationship with books, and the library that bears his name, was more capricious. Like the contents of a Renaissance cabinet (see p. 12), Wellcome's nascent gatherings of books and artefacts blurred into one. In his London home, he wrote to his mother, he desired space to have 'books and things about me'; in his office, hunting trophies rubbed shoulders with general literature.

In a commercial context, books were initially the more useful acquisitions, providing a bank of design ideas that might help this American pharmaceuticals man win business in a competitive market. After Silas Burroughs's death, Wellcome's own motivations became more research-focused. His interest in the content of individual books waned and his overwhelming vision became the accumulation of as complete a collection of objects and publications as possible.

Wellcome's insatiable appetite for acquiring objects also outweighed any inclination to sort, catalogue or even use the books he approved for purchase. As Wellcome's collection grew, books might stay in the boxes they had been shipped in for years, or even decades. For all of Wellcome's life, his library was also inaccessible to the public.

ABOVE: **Interior of Burroughs Wellcome & Co. headquarters, Snow Hill, designed by Sir Henry Wellcome**
Pencil drawing
1885
23491i Wellcome Library

⌒

[The office] is furnished as a library, although hunting trophies, works of art from centres visited by the occupant, a striking statuette of Henry Ward Beecher, and a varied selection of general literature give it less the look of a commercial room and more the appearance of a bachelor's den.

Chemist & Druggist describing Henry Wellcome's office in the Burroughs Wellcome premises at Snow Hill, 1888

🖉 Inspiring design

**Burroughs Wellcome price list
1885–91**
L0076891 Wellcome Images

Wellcome's early book-buying focused on sourcing typography and design inspiration for Burroughs Wellcome's own marketing and packaging materials. The company's first 'book room' at its Snow Hill offices included almanacs and atlases, embroidery patterns and albums of architectural motifs.

🖉 An ambitious undertaking

In the 1890s, Wellcome conceived a plan to research and publish an encyclopaedic book, a chronicle of human ingenuity that would document the use of animal products in medicine from antiquity to contemporary times. His ambitious aim would be achieved by collecting books and artefacts and empirically testing the chemistry of various substances. Wellcome's work was never completed, but his vision drove the eclectic growth of the library for many years. It also led to the recruitment of its first librarian, pharmacy graduate and writer Charles John Samuel Thompson (1862–1943).

**Peacock
Painting on silk from *Bencao Tupu*
(*Illustrated Herbal*), 1630
Zhou Rongqi**
L0039441 Wellcome Images

This illustration for an unpublished 'herbal' from the Chinese Ming period depicts a peacock, once used to treat ulcers, abscesses and drug poisoning.

Early investments

The first official acquisition C J S Thompson made for Wellcome's library was a seventeenth-century collection of medicinal recipes by Lady Ayscough, bought in 1897. A year later, he made the company's first major book purchase at auction, acquiring 482 lots from William Morris's library at Sotheby's for the sum of £1843 9s 6d. Not long after, Thompson was formally appointed to care for the company's growing mass of books. The first and longest-serving of Wellcome's collecting collaborators, Thompson would remain head of the Library for 13 years, before becoming Curator of the Wellcome Historical Medical Museum.

We may say that the last idea is that you shall be known as 'librarian'.

Wellcome's secretary writing to C J S Thompson in 1899

C J S Thompson
L0013410 Wellcome Images

An aggravating bidder

An early acquisitions coup was the 1911 purchase of the library of medical historian and librarian to the Royal College of Physicians Dr J F Payne (1840–1910). Rich in incunabula, early herbals and plague literature, the collection was also a target for Canadian physician Sir William Osler (1849–1919), who had been commissioned to buy it on behalf of Johns Hopkins School of Medicine.

Frank Payne bookplate
L0021429 Wellcome Images

Osler reported in *Bibliotheca Osleriana* that Payne's library 'was lost for the School in an aggravating way' after the Sotheby's lot was knocked down to an unknown bidder within a minute. Osler was magnanimous in defeat: 'I am glad for the sake of Dr Payne's memory that it has been kept together and will be well housed in the Wellcome Historical Museum'. Osler also managed to accumulate his own collection of 8000 books, now housed at the Osler Library of the History of Medicine, which opened at McGill University in 1929.

'Like stout Cortez'

Originally located with the Wellcome Historical Medical Museum in London's Wigmore Street, the Library was separated from its sister institution in 1921, when it moved to nearby premises in Stratford Mews. It remained there for seven years, never opening to the public.

In 1928, the Library moved once again, to a spacious former wireless factory on the Hythe Road industrial estate at Willesden Junction. No readers were allowed to visit, though postal enquiries were handled. Much of the staff's time was spent unpacking, cataloguing and sorting consignments of books that had been sitting unopened for years. Noël Poynter, who joined as a junior assistant in 1930 and rose to be Director of the Museum and Library, likened disturbing 'the dust of years' on these 'heaped mounds of books' to the explorations of a new world by 'stout Cortez'.

The double helix

In 2002, 11 filing cabinets filled with the professional papers of Francis Crick (1916–2004). arrived at the Wellcome Library from California. It was the first batch of thousands of notes, drafts and correspondence acquired from the co-discoverer of the double-helical structure of DNA, who later worked in molecular biology, neuroscience and brain research. The third and final batch of Crick's papers was finally catalogued in 2011 and the entire archive has also been digitised.

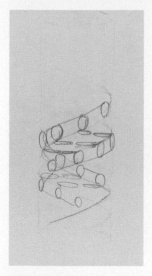

The DNA double helix
Pencil
Francis Crick, 1953
B0004367 Wellcome Images

Custom-made classification

When young Cyril C Barnard (1894–1959) was tasked with choosing a classification system for 'a very special library' in 1921, he found the standard Dewey decimal and Brown subject classifications unsuitable for a medical collection. Barnard's desire to locate the anatomy, physiology, pathology and surgery of one organ in a single location (rather than four), drove him to spend years developing his own system.

The alphabetically based Barnard system splits medicine into a range of subjects (such as history, epidemiology, toxicology or surgery) that can be sub-divided into organs or other subsets. Most topics can then be represented by just two letters. For example, BM indicates anatomy, VG is anaesthesia and UJ covers psychological medicine.

A decade after leaving Wellcome, Barnard set out his work in his 1931 thesis for the Library Association's Diploma with Honours, later published as *A Classification for Medical Libraries with Introduction, Local List,*

Index of Parasites and General Index (1936). Barnard's system is still used to classify the Library's medical publications.

From statues to books

Hall of Statuary, Wigmore Street
1926
M0020277 Wellcome Images

When the Wellcome Historical Medical Museum opened in Wigmore Street in 1913, as the official museum of the 17th International Congress of Medicine, the galleried Hall of Statuary was its most impressive room. Featuring statues of medical deities, a model of a Greek temple, amulets, surgical instruments and reproductions from medical manuscripts, it also included a specially commissioned series of paintings depicting great moments in medicine. Two decades later, a larger version of the Hall was designed when the Museum relocated to today's neoclassical building at 183 Euston Road, designed by Septimus Warwick (1881–1954).

Hall of Statuary stairs, Euston Road
Photograph
M0004497 Wellcome Images

Hall of Statuary, Euston Road
M0004496 Wellcome Images

📎 Changing roles

In 1941, five years after Wellcome's death, the newly named Wellcome Historical Medical Library was reunited with the Museum after two decades apart. Allocated the Hall of Statuary space at Euston Road just months after the Blitz, packed cases of books were deployed next to the windows as blast ballast. Though readers were admitted by appointment from 1946, the library didn't open to the public until 1949, and had to make do with temporary fittings and furniture until the mid 1950s.

When the Museum was temporarily dismantled to make way for offices in 1946, the roles of the book and object collections reversed. The Library acquired – at least for a few years – the more prominent position in the public's eye.

My plans exist in my mind like a jigsaw puzzle, and gradually I shall be able to piece it together.

Henry Wellcome, c.1934

It is indeed difficult to say what this Museum, with its contents and a library of more than 100 000 books, manuscripts and incunabula so quietly amassed, will mean to medicine in the future.

From Sir Humphry Rolleston's introductory speech at the reopening ceremony of the Wellcome Historical Medical Museum, 1926

📖 Read

Battles M. Library: An unquiet history. New York: Norton; 2003.

Campbell JWP. The Library: A world history. London: Thames & Hudson; 2013.

Gould T. Cures & Curiosities: Inside the Wellcome Library. London: Profile; 2007.

Larson F. An Infinity of Things: How Sir Henry Wellcome collected the world. Oxford: Oxford University Press; 2009.

Hall of Statuary adapted for the Library
*c.*1960
29167i Wellcome Library

Library Reading Room after reconstruction
1962
29207i Wellcome Library

Library Reading Room
2007
C0034792 Wellcome Images

Natural history museum
of Ferrante Imperato of Naples
Engraving
From *Historia Naturale di Ferrante Imperato
Napolitano: Nella quale ordinatamente si tratta
della diversa condition di minere, pietre pretiose,
ed altre curiosità*, **1672**
b13064290 Wellcome Library

📎 A reminder of the Renaissance

The current Reading Room unites the space's past lives
as library and gallery. Together, these functions invoke
something of the spirit of the early modern library or
cabinet, in which books and objects were intermingled
and visitors could engage in solitary study or convivial
debate.

**The Royal Medical and Chirurgical Society
of London library and meeting room**
From *The Royal Medical and Chirurgical
Society of London: Centenary 1805–1905*, **1905**
N Moore and S Paget
b10710486 Wellcome Library

Renovation below the Reading Room frieze
2014
Wellcome Images

Reading Room under renovation
2014
Wellcome Images

Subject index

Caption index

Reading Room credits

Reading Room team

Ken Arnold
Ruth Blue
Virginie Cerdeira
Simon Chaplin
Anna Faherty
Georgia Monk
Julia Nurse
Vicki Porter
Oliver Vicars-Harris
Oliver Winchester

Architects: AOC
Main contractor: MER Services Ltd.
Lighting: DHA Designs
Graphic design: Objectif
Visualisation table: Interactive Institute C Studio
Facsimile book production: Book Works
Lenders: Adamson Trust Collection; Eleanor Crook,
Pitt Rivers Museum, University of Oxford;
Science Museum, London.

Thanks to

Clara Ahlvik, Hugh Aldersey-Williams, Marion Akehurst,
Daniel Antoine, Kate Arnold-Forster, Ian Blatchford, Tim Boon,
Colin Bowles Ltd, Steve Britt, Chris Bunker, Camira Fabrics,
Emily Candler, Seb Chan, Complete Fabrication, Constantine,
Jago Cooper, Jack Craig, Luke Currall, Sal Davies, Alex Drew,
Joanna Ebenstein, Freud Museum, Ruth Garde, Granville &
Burbidge, GV Art gallery, Elaine Heumann Gurion, Simon Hillson,
Jane Holmes, Peter King, Christian Kingham, Rosalind Leake,
Jane Macnaughton, Meyvaert UK Ltd, Benjamin Moreno,
Yutaka Nakano, Neutral Digital, James Peto, Plowden & Smith,
Alastair Reid, SCP, Jon Stokes, Abby Taylor, John Taylor,
Ryan Todd, Catherine Walker, John Watson, Jane Wildgoose.

And all the staff of the Wellcome Library, including

Richard Aspin, Laurie Auchterlonie, Briony Benge-Abbot,
Gillian Boal, Sarah Bond, Tom Cox, Rowan De Saulles,
Richard Everett, Tom Farnetti, Crestina Forcina,
Luana Franceschet, Ben Gilbert, Amy Junker Heslip,
Kath Knowles, Meghan Lambert, Stephen Lowther,
Ross Macfarlane, Damian Nicolaou, Jette Nielsen,
Anna Ostrowska, Steven Pocock, Daniel Rees,
Angela Saward, William Schupbach, Nikolai Serikoff,
Stefania Signorello, Joe Simmonds-Isler.